QUEEN MARGARET COLLEGE
CORSTORPHINE CAMPUS LIBRARY

———

Please return book by date stamped below

GW00535927

Fertility Counselling

Fertility Counselling

Sue Mack BA, CQSW,
Dip. Counselling

and

Julie Tucker RM, ADM,
Dip. Counselling

Baillière Tindall

PUBLISHED IN ASSOCIATION WITH THE RCN

London   Philadelphia   Sydney   Tokyo   Toronto

Baillière Tindall   24–28 Oval Road
W.B. Saunders Company Ltd London NW1 7DX

The Curtis Center
Independence Square West
Philadelphia, PA 19106–3399, USA

Harcourt Brace & Company
55 Horner Avenue
Toronto, Ontario, M8Z 4X6, Canada

Harcourt Brace & Company, Australia
30–52 Smidmore Street
Marrickville
NSW 2204, Australia

Harcourt Brace & Company, Japan
Ichibancho Central Building
Chiyoda-ku, Tokyo 102, Japan

A catalogue record for this book is available from the British Library

ISBN 0–7020–1977–1

Typeset by Laserscript, Mitcham, Surrey
Printed and bound in Great Britain by WBC Book Manufacturers
Limited, Bridgend, Mid Glamorgan.

Contents

Introduction

One in six couples in Britain are known to share the pain and distress of infertility; we do not know how many suffer without adding to the statistics. This pain begins from the time they recognize that they may not be able to have their own children through diagnosis, investigations and treatment. They may receive excellent support, advice and counselling throughout, or they may not. They will certainly experience a wide spectrum of feelings, which can be helped by skilled counselling.

This book is based around the expressed needs of individuals facing infertility, at all stages from recognition to pregnancy or the decision not to have children. These are from our own experience as counsellors, from discussions with a large number of individuals and couples for this book and from the extensive replies to a questionnaire (see Appendix). These couples wanted to help us understand their feelings with the hope that this would help others in their situation.

Current Practice

In the UK, legislation in the form of the Human Fertilization and Embryology Act governs clinical and research practice within the assisted conception clinics. The terms of reference of the Human Fertilization and Embryology Authority (HFEA) have widespread implications for both the clinicians and the patients who come for treatment. These are considered as well as the provision of service and the professionals involved within the UK. Current practice in other countries is also reviewed, giving some insight into different societal and cultural demands placed on couples and individuals.

Medical Practice

Medical practice is changing all the time, as research identifies new areas amenable to treatment and as practice is developed and redefined. Medical intervention is examined from the initial involvement of the general practitioner (GP) to the sophisticated techniques of specialist centres. The procedures, from investigations to treatment and other options are considered in terms of the process, risks and outcomes.

Infertility is a rapidly changing specialty and there have been huge scientific advances that have informed practice, yet a third of all couples are still given the diagnosis of 'unexplained infertility' and the highest recorded rate of success in terms of a live baby is less than 40%.

The Psychological Effects

Infertile individuals are part of a society that recognizes parenting as a normal expectation for adults and is often unwilling to commit resources to treatment. The effects on the individual, couple and community of infertility and medical interventions are considered at all stages of the process from the desire to parent to the possibility of alternative parenthood and pregnancy.

Counselling Theory and Skills

Counselling theories illustrate the range of help available to those who offer counselling as well as those who receive it. The skills apply to all counselling practice as well as to counsellors who may see infertile individuals in GP surgeries, clinics and private practice.

Who can be the Counsellor?

Since the HFEA requires counselling to be offered with treatment, most people going through the process will encounter counselling at some stage, and most clinics will offer such help.

Counselling may be regarded by some professionals as no more than having a chat and this may satisfy the client's needs; for others it will be therapeutic counselling offered by a skilled, trained helper. Between these two extremes are the support, implications and information counselling that is required by the HFEA and which may be undertaken by various members of the healthcare team.

The Needs of the Client

The needs of the client as expressed to us have informed the way we have approached the subject and are at the heart of this book. Their unmet need for counselling help or at least a counselling approach, from the earliest recognition of the problem right through to parenthood or the decision not to parent, has guided the way we have considered the counselling skills and approach that may help.

Counselling for Infertility

The experience of infertility does not necessarily demand therapeutic counselling from beginning to end. Clients express different needs at different times, even within the couple relationship. The awareness of these needs and differences enables all those concerned with infertility to offer the most appropriate support, information and counselling.

Names and identifiable details have been changed to preserve anonymity, but all the stories we have recorded are as they were told to us and, where quoted, are in the words of the clients. Whilst we have addressed the gender differences in attitudes toward infertility and counselling, we have tried not to make assumptions on the basis of race, gender or sexual orientation.

We must express our thanks to Issue for their help with research, our fellow professionals, who were a constant source of support and information, and most of all the individuals and couples who gave their time to share their feelings, hopes and fears with us with a wish that it will help others.

Chapter 1

Overview of Current Practice in the UK and Other Countries

Public concern with the medical and scientific technology of the assisted conception techniques, especially *in vitro* fertilization (IVF), has given the subject of infertility a high profile since the birth of Louise Brown in July 1978. At that point, what was known and practiced in the animal world was made possible for the human species. When such a large area which has important medical, scientific and ethical implications opens up, society expects some guiding principles to be brought to bear on the subject for its protection. The spectre of scientists in the laboratory carrying out unknown and unregulated experiments without control sparked off much controversy.

In the UK the Government started the process of regulation in 1982 by setting up a committee under the chairmanship of Dame Mary Warnock to inquire into the subject of human fertilization and embryology. The committee's terms of reference were:

'To consider recent and potential developments in medicine and science related to human fertilization and embryology; to consider what

1

> *policies and safeguards should be applied,*
> *including consideration of the ethical and legal*
> *implications of these developments, and to make*
> *recommendations' (Warnock 1988, p. 4).*

The members of this committee consulted with all who were involved with human fertilization and embryology and those within society who held strong views for or against the development of therapeutic and scientific practices. The aim was to incorporate the views from varied backgrounds into legislation so that this would reflect societal concerns and values.

The committee enquired into the use of techniques to alleviate the suffering of infertility including the medical techniques employed, the use of donated sperm eggs and embryos, and surrogacy. They then made recommendations as to the practice and regulation of treatments. In considering the wider debate concerning storage and research on gametes and embryos, they sought to control and set limits on such storage and research that would be acceptable to society. They recognized that the pace of scientific discovery is rapid. Anxiety was generated in the public mind about the scope of the scientific endeavours and so recommendations were set to give guidance in the practical sense, to offer suggestions about changes and to make the clarification required in the law.

Whilst taking evidence from around 300 people and organizations, the intent of the committee was not to consider every situation that may occur but to consider 'the fundamental questions raised in relation to any existing law' (Warnock 1988, p. 7) and offer suggestions for essential legislative changes. The list of recommendations fell under the headings of:

- a licensing body and its functions
- principles of provision
- service provision
- legal limits on research
- legal changes.

Warnock recognized that couples with infertility had emotional needs that were not being attended to. In the comprehen-

2

sive list of recommendations they stated that 'Counselling should be available to all infertile couples and third parties at any stage of the treatment, both as an integral part of NHS provision and in the private sector' (Warnock 1988, p. 82). The environment of care was also felt to be of some importance and it was recommended that clinics be separate from other types of gynaecology clinics where possible.

Surrogacy arrangements raised debate within the committee. There were two expressions of dissent for this method of achieving parenthood but the recommendation was to include rather than exclude. The ethical dilemmas around the use of embryos in research gave rise to much public debate. Warnock sought to express the arguments for and against which centred around the status of the embryo. A human embryo can be seen as having the potential for life and therefore some degree of respect is due, but the law does not afford an embryo the right to life. The embryo in biological terms is a collection of cells which, unless implantation occurs, has no potential for growth. If the latter is the case then there is no reason to confer any protective status on the embryo. The majority view came out in favour of permitting research but using a framework of legislation to set limits of practice, which were felt at the time to respond to a general consensus within society.

After the report of the Warnock committee came a public consultation process which helped frame the Human Fertilization and Embryology Bill put before Parliament in 1990. In the meantime, to give some support and guidance to those working within this new field, the Medical Research Council and the Royal College of Obstetricians and Gynaecologists set up what became known as the Voluntary Licensing Authority (VLA) in 1985. These bodies acknowledged the necessity for a regulating body and were able to prepare guidelines for good practice that would be generally consistent with Government recommendations finally enshrined within the Human Fertilization and Embryology Act. The VLA changed to the Interim Licensing Authority (ILA) and each year published results of treatments for those clinics that sent in their data. Whilst clinics were encouraged to report to them with research information, treatment methods and success rates, they were under no obligation to do so. In these years there was no uniformity in the data collected by infertility clinics and people seeking treatment were given a variety of statistics, which led to much confusion. The ILA, whilst attempting to monitor clinics, did not have the authority to take action if clinics were not functioning at acceptable levels of good practice.

In 1990, after much press attention and lobbying from the Pro-life lobby who focused on ethical dilemmas around embryo research and the point at which human life begins, the Human Fertilization and Embryology Act passed onto the statute books.

The King's Fund Centre was asked by the Department of Health to consider the counselling requirements of those seeking what would be regulated infertility treatments. Their terms of reference were:

> *'To provide advice for the consideration of the Human Fertilization and Embryology Authority on the counselling needs relating to the provision of infertility services for couples considering any of the regulated infertility treatments; for children born following gametes and embryo donation who seek information about their origins, and for all donors' (King's Fund Centre 1991).*

The HFEA Code of Practice (1995b) adopted their approach to the provision of counselling, choosing to apply the broad headings of:

- implications counselling
- support counselling
- therapeutic counselling.

The Code of Practice seeks to differentiate this from the normal information-giving process that applies to everyone, including the offer of professional advice and any assessment that may be made in order to determine if treatment should be offered.

THE HUMAN FERTILIZATION AND EMBRYOLOGY ACT

The Act makes provision:

> *'in connection with human embryos and any subsequent development of such embryos;*
>
> - *to prohibit certain practices in connection with embryos and gametes;*
> - *to establish a Human Fertilization and Embryology Authority;*
> - *to make provision about the persons who in certain circumstances are to be treated in law as the parents of a child; and*
> - *to amend the Surrogacy Arrangements Act 1985.'*

Prohibition in Connection with Gametes and Embryos

Activities governed by this part of the Act relate to the handling and storage of oocytes, sperm and embryos in the laboratory of a licensed clinic. Research may only be carried out on embryos up to the end of the 14th day after the gametes were mixed. The primitive streak is formed at this time and marks the beginning of individual development for the embryo. The Act prohibits trans-species transfer of human embryos and cloning.

HUMAN FERTILIZATION AND EMBRYOLOGY AUTHORITY (HFEA)

From the embryo of the ILA came a statutory body that was required to grant licences, define and monitor good practice, maintain a register, publish statistics relating to treatment success rates, and report to the Secretary of State for Health on its activities. It consists of 21 members representing medical, scientific, nursing, social, legal, lay and religious views.

5

General Functions of the Authority

The functions of the HFEA are to:

- 'keep under review information about embryos and any subsequent development of embryos and about the provision of treatment services and activities governed by this Act, and advise the Secretary of State, if he asks it to do so, about those matters;
- publicize the services provided to the public by the Authority or provided in pursuance of licences;
- provide, to such extent as it considers appropriate, advice and information for persons to whom licences apply or who are receiving treatment services or providing gametes or embryos for the purposes of activities governed by this Act, or may wish to do so, and perform such other functions as may be specified in regulations'.

(HFE Act 1990, p. 4)

Because gamete intra-fallopian transfer (GIFT) does not involve handling of gametes, it is excluded from licensing requirements. It is not necessarily governed by the guidelines and Code of Practice of the HFEA. District General Hospitals are able to offer this form of treatment, often without the support required to help the couple to understand the implications of the proposed treatment and to cope with the distress of failure of treatment. The debate around including GIFT within the Act still continues. As the procedure does not involve the creation of embryos outside the human body the strict regulations of the HFE Act do not apply. The only restriction that the HFEA does feel able to apply is the regulation that only three oocytes should be transferred to a woman in one treatment cycle. However, if GIFT is performed with donated sperm then the Act does apply. It seems illogical that the same rules are not applied, because the woman is exposed to the same medical, social and ethical risks as IVF and, in some cases, without the opportunity to learn of fertilization of spare eggs or facilities for cryopreserving excess embryos. Clinics that offer a range of high technology treatments will offer their clients the same care and support as those undergoing licensed treatments, but where no such control is in place, there is a danger that couples will not receive the appropriate level of nursing and counselling support they would have as a matter of course if they were having IVF.

In 1994 the HFEA sent out questionnaires to all NHS consultants registered with the Royal College of Obstetricians and Gynaecologists about the provision of GIFT. The results of that survey showed that 'most GIFT was carried out in HFEA registered clinics where there is no evidence of inappropriate use' (HFEA 1995a, p. 21). As the HFEA now feels that there may be within the HFE Act the ability to invoke regulatory powers to make GIFT a licensable activity, the HFEA has passed their information to the Department of Health for the Government to decide whether this is necessary.

Licensing Clinics

Inspectors are recruited by the HFEA to visit each centre applying for a license or carrying out licensable activities. The list of inspectors comprises people from within the professions involved in infertility and related scientific, social and ethical areas. They report back to the licensing and fees committee, which is specifically concerned with the granting, suspension and revocation of licences.

The inspectors and the committee monitor licensed centres. These centres may undertake research without clinical treatment of infertility, or may offer donor insemination (DI), storage of sperm or the full range of reproductive treatments. Practical issues such as the environment of care and the medical standards maintained will be assessed, as well as the associated legal, scientific, social, ethical and moral aspects of care. The licensing committee can be seen as society's watchdog.

Licenses are required for the following specific activities:

- IVF treatment
- any fertility treatment involving donated human eggs or sperm, which could include GIFT using donor sperm
- storage of human eggs, sperm or embryos for treatment or for research, and embryo research (HFEA 1994, p. 21).

To receive a license a clinic has to submit to the committee all treatment, medical, scientific and, if appropriate, research protocols, and papers relating to patient information. All the staff involved in caring for the patients need to register their curriculum vitae. The committee will review the paperwork and set up an inspection visit.

The inspection team consists of four people, one of whom will be a member of the HFEA. The function of the team is to become familiar with the working practices and procedures within the clinics initially in order to be able to grant a license. Thereafter, yearly visits are made to monitor and ensure high standards of practice. The licensing committee of the HFEA, on the recommendation of the team, may revoke a license or suspend a clinic and they have the authority to refuse applications. In its Fourth Annual Report, the HFEA (1995a) has stated its intention to widen the scope of the inspection teams so that they may use information gained from 'other sources', for instance the HFEA register, to help make decisions about reviewing licenses. They also plan to make different kinds of visits, which may be at short notice or unannounced, or more in-depth concentrating on particular issues. After all, formal planned visits allow for much preparation and the inspectors may not see the normal day-to-day running of the clinic as they might wish.

Code of Practice

The Code of Practice, already revised in 1993 and 1995, is in effect the law in action. It sets out guidance for the proper conduct of the licensed centres in such matters as staffing, facilities, assessment of clients, donors and the welfare of the child, information, consent, counselling, use of gametes and embryos, storage and handling of gametes and embryos, research, records and complaints.

The code of practice committee will investigate any breaches of the HFE Act or the Code of Practice. These breaches may constitute criminal offences, which would be referred to the Director of Public Prosecutions. There is a named 'person responsible' at each clinic and he/she is held to be liable for misconduct and may be prosecuted for breaches of the Code.

Each year the HFEA looks in depth at particular issues related to research and treatments, and consultation documents are circulated to all interested parties. Topics such as the use of fetal ovarian tissue attracted much publicity and excited public debate in 1994. Working groups have been set up to consider other areas of concern such as the information given to those receiving treatment and the training of infertility counsellors. The HFEA may ask that practice be changed following appropriate recommendations from these groups.

Whilst the law is very clear about what it demands of assisted conception clinics, it has no part in practices at the start of investigations. It is in this area, almost before the issue of treatment arises, that many couples feel lost and alone without the information they need to help them through.

TREATMENT ISSUES

The HFE Act has opened up the treatment of infertility and some of the options have given rise to public discussion and debate. Everyone has a view on many of the available treatments. The following are some of the areas covered by the Act and the Code of Practice that will continue to be somewhat controversial and may require that changes be made within the law.

Donation of Gametes

The Code of Practice sets out clear guidelines as to who can be donors, both male and female. Difficulty with recruitment has led some to suggest that the limit of 10 offspring per male donor (HFE Act 1990) be increased to 20 without increasing the remote risk of a future half-sibling relationship (Leiberman *et al.* 1994, p. 1781). The limits apply to gametes and embryos, but in special circumstances, i.e. where a recipient wishes to have another child from the same donor, this limit may be exceeded provided the HFEA is notified. In practice this causes great problems for the clinicians and prompt and accurate information regarding pregnancy and outcome is necessary between donor banks and their users to ensure that they comply with the Code of Practice.

Payment may be given to the donors of sperm, eggs or embryos 'up to £15 per donation plus reasonable expenses'. This most commonly applies to sperm donors but the HFEA included

9

in their direction that women may be 'offered benefits in the form of treatment services or free sterilization in exchange for donating eggs'. Women undertake a potentially more hazardous treatment to retrieve eggs and may expect more rewards for their donation; others prefer to donate on a purely altruistic basis. In practice this has made the recruiting of egg donors a hard task and women who require this treatment are encouraged to find a woman who would donate either to them or anonymously to another woman. This in effect moves the woman who needs the donation up the queue towards treatment. Anonymity of the donor is preserved in many cases but known donors may also be used because of the lack of a donor pool.

Cryopreservation

Cryopreservation of embryos has become more successful over the past few years and is now available in most clinics. In the private sector, treatment with cryopreserved embryos costs a little less than a complete IVF cycle with the added benefit to the woman of little or no intervention and in some cases no medication is used. The pregnancy rates are lower at 9–17% (HFEA 1995a, p. 46) but there appear to be no increased risks of miscarriage or congenital abnormality. The length of the statutory storage period was initially set at 5 years. This was a somewhat arbitrary length of time allowing for prompt review and flexibility for Parliamentary changes. In 1996 some embryos will have reached their 5-year limit and couples will be asked to reassess their situation. Parliament will also be making clear its decisions and the law may require amendment.

Number of Embryos Replaced

There has been a move to reduce the number of embryos that can be replaced in any one treatment cycle. The upper limit of three may yet have an effect on the numbers of triplets born, which was rising before the HFEA brought in this recommendation. Multiple pregnancy brings with it risks of prematurity and increases the perinatal death rate from 1% for singletons to 4.7% for triplets (HFEA 1995a, p. 31). Pregnancy rates do not appear to differ significantly when there is a choice between two and three embryos, but the incidence of triplet pregnancies can be influenced greatly (Morgan *et al.* 1996, p. 19a).

Pre-implantation Diagnosis

Detection of some genetic defects is a reality and more genes are being identified as the human genome map develops. Pre-implantation diagnosis entails the removal of one or more cells from an embryo, preferably at the blastocyst stage, for genetic analysis. Only one HFEA laboratory is applying this technique in practice (HFEA 1994, p. 32). Couples who are known to be at risk of passing on genetic disease could avoid the painful decision, after diagnosis in pregnancy, to terminate an affected fetus. It is possible to detect single gene defects such as cystic fibrosis, chromosomal abnormalities such as trisomy 21 (Down's syndrome) and sex-linked diseases such as Duchenne muscular dystrophy (DMD) and select only the normally developing embryos for transfer (Handyside 1992). The hope is that if only genetically intact embryos are replaced, the pregnancy rate with IVF will increase.

Surrogacy

Non-commercial surrogacy is allowed in law. The Surrogacy Arrangements Act 1985 was amended by the HFE Act in 1990. Anxiety and controversy have surrounded this part of the Act as it is seen to be putting all those who undertake surrogacy arrangements at substantial emotional risk. Likewise the commissioning couple have no recourse in law to claim their child from the surrogate as the Act particularly states that 'no surrogacy arrangement is enforceable by or against any of the persons making it' (HFE Act 1990, section 32.1A). Where there is dispute over custody of the child, the child's best interest will take precedence over the rights of the parents.

Following on from this it was seen to be necessary to set out the regulations by which legal parental responsibility can be transferred from birth parents to commissioning parents (HFE Act, section 30). Before this change, the commissioning parents were required in law to formally adopt their own child.

Surrogacy may not require the intervention of a third party, i.e. a fertility clinic, and informal arrangements have been made long before the reproductive technologies were possible (Genesis, ch. 16). With the advent of IVF it became possible to use the commissioning woman's own eggs, fertilize them with her partner's sperm and place the resulting embryos in the surrogate woman's womb. This has been referred to as 'host motherhood', the resulting child being genetically related to both commissioning parents instead of only the father. The same steps of giving up a baby and taking on parenthood give rise to many of the same emotional issues and will determine outcomes for all involved. Careful preparation of all the individuals concerned is encouraged with access to clear and relevant information (British Medical Association 1996, p. 3) and in many cases the clinic will have clear guidelines of what they expects both couples to undergo before embarking on this potentially hazardous form of treatment.

Welfare of the Child

This is a difficult concept for the infertile to grasp as the child concerned is not and may never be real. The most recent Code of Practice expands on the theme in its earlier issues and gives a list of factors to be considered and enquiries to be made when contemplating offering treatment (HFEA 1995b, sections 3.15–3.27). Some centres are adopting formal procedures of asking prospective clients to complete medical and social questionnaires when they are first referred, and asking them to have their GP complete forms as well. Failure or refusal may result in no offer of treatment, so those with issues in the past may wish to conceal important details from the licensed clinic. Those presenting for treatment may already be dealing with issues around isolation and rejection. It can be argued that those who conceive spontaneously do not have their parenting abilities assessed. The case for assessment for adoption differs in that there is a child who has already had severe disruption to his/her life and care needs to be taken that as far as possible this is not repeated. Society, however, needs to be sure that safeguards are in place for protection of children and that the institution of the family is not violated.

Success Rates

In October 1995 the HFEA published a *Patient's Guide to DI and IVF Clinics* (HFEA 1995c). Contained within are details from each licensed clinic about the number of treatment cycles undertaken in 1 year and the outcome in terms of pregnancy rates, percentage of multiple pregnancies, and live birth rate. There is a need to inform potential clients about their chances of taking a baby home after treatment to enable them to make choices about where they go for treatment. Unfortunately, as most of the clinics cited are in the private sector, access to them may be impossible for some because of either accessibility or financial implications. The HFEA does point out that the live birth rate is not the only factor to be considered when deciding on a clinic, but it is the stated goal of those seeking treatment. There may be other important issues such as the provision of certain forms of treatment known to be necessary such as GIFT or ICSI (intracytoplasmic sperm injection) or the environment and situation of the clinic that determine choice.

Provision of Service

The scope and organization of infertility services up to the time of the new technological advances was poorly coordinated and, whilst able to lead to diagnosis, little in the way of treatment was on offer. Warnock's committee did feel that infertility is a condition meriting treatment but it has been largely left to the professionals already concerned with delivering a service and the infertile themselves to make demands for the service they need within the NHS. The Act offers no directive to purchasers of health about what or which service to purchase and so it may be viewed that, given that the budget for health care is not limitless, society is not prepared to prioritize fertility treatments. The growth of private clinics, where treatment costs vary, contributes to a feeling that whilst the NHS is prepared to offer diagnosis through GPs, Family Planning and hospital clinics, it is, generally, not willing or able to bear the cost of treatment.

Since the provider–purchaser split within the NHS, some commissioning health authorities have reviewed the services on offer in their district and made decisions about the purchase of fertility services. Some have adopted formal clinical guidelines governing the treatment to be offered. For some, the infertility services provided in the NHS hospital will be covered by a block contract for gynaecology and will not be costed out separately. The true cost of an infertility service will have been hidden and data relating to *ad hoc* services may not be available. The disparity between the variety and scope of services offered leads to couples having no clear information about what they can expect to be offered as part of their diagnosis and treatment. If they have no clear expectation of what they should be receiving then they become confused and alienated. It is at the level of investigations that expertise needs to be directed to ensure that each couple has an understanding of the implications of the proposed action so that they may make decisions appropriately. The HFEA has no remit to regulate or monitor care at this level. The fertility specialists within the RCOG have expressed concern about effective and appropriate investigations and issue guidelines both through the RCOG and the British Fertility Society in an effort to standardize the tests and investigations required for the diagnosis and management of infertility. In this way the most efficient use of resources is made.

Provision of NHS Assisted Conception Techniques

In 1994 the College of Health published a report commissioned by the National Infertility Awareness Campaign on funding and provision of infertility services within the UK (this report has been updated for 1995). Ninety-eight Health Authorities responded to a postal questionnaire enquiring into their purchasing agreements and intentions. Some clearly had no knowledge of what was available and some had carried out reviews and their purchasing intentions were clear.

This report demonstrated that there is still a great variation in the level of funding and services throughout the UK. Where the services are not provided within the Health Authority some have chosen to purchase treatments from either NHS or private assisted conception clinics on an extracontractual referral basis. Selection criteria may be set for this by the purchaser, such as the 'woman must be in a stable relationship, the woman must not have been previously sterilized' (College of Health 1994, p. 32). These are not

14

clinical guidelines based on medical criteria. The disparity between the Health Authorities demonstrates unequal service provision based on widely differing criteria resulting in couples or individuals having access to NHS assisted conception treatment dependent on geographical and social reasons, rather than need.

Lack of provision of local services within the NHS increases the stress felt by many and it may mean that they no longer pursue treatment. Where there are services available, a range of selection criteria may be used. The age of the female partner is a common factor that can be linked to the possibility of successful outcome given that there are limited resources. Some areas have clearly indicated that being in a stable relationship or, in some instances, married is an important criterion for them. Others seem concerned to ensure that neither partner has living children with the aim of giving everyone a chance. The issue of treating single women or those in a homosexual relationship has not been explicit and, as in surrogacy, can often be left to local ethical committees for decisions. It appears that both medical and social criteria pertain in a haphazard fashion and that once these have been laid down there is little likelihood of change.

Funding

There has been a call from the professionals involved for the HFEA to be centrally funded. At the moment the authority is expected to raise 50% of its costs through the fees levied for the granting of licences and treatment cycles. Those receiving licensed treatments pay a fixed amount to the HFEA for each treatment cycle. This has been dubbed an 'unfair tax on the infertile' (Bolton and Parsons 1991, p. 309; Hewitt 1991, p. 244). It seems unlikely that the plea to be centrally funded will receive attention for the time being.

THE PROFESSIONAL TEAM

The disciplines working in assisted reproduction come from a variety of backgrounds and as the specialism grew so did the need for developing training pathways under the guidance of the individual professional bodies concerned.

15

Nursing

The training and educational needs of nurses were recognized with the establishment of the Assisted Conception Course ENB N40, which has been running since 1994. The course is run by the Institute of Advanced Nursing Education (IANE) at the Royal College of Nursing. Nurses work with those with fertility problems in a variety of settings including gynaecology wards and clinics, assisted conception clinics, GP surgeries and Family Planning clinics. Their role within these areas differs and has extended as they take on ultrasound scanning or counselling as part of their practice.

Medical Staff

The medical team come from a common background and experience but may have chosen a particular focus to their clinical work. GPs, Family Planning doctors, obstetricians and gynaecologists, andrologists and reproductive endocrinologists are the most common specialities that link to infertility. Urologists may well be involved in male infertility, and especially as sperm retrieval techniques advance may have more input into the team. In training for their specialty, doctors will have all worked with fertility but it may be from one particular aspect. The RCOG is currently looking into training that will allow for these disparities. A group of centres offers subspecialty training in reproductive medicine with accreditation by the RCOG (Barlow 1992, p. 390). The RCOG publishes guidelines for practice prepared by the Fertility Committee that offer clear pathways through investigation at GP level, referral to a specialist unit, diagnosis and treatment, and suggestions for audit of services.

Scientific Staff

Embryology has developed from being a biological and research activity to a clinical laboratory practice. The Association of Clinical Embryologists (ACE) was formed with one of its main objectives being the setting up of a formal training and accreditation scheme. With this in mind a post-graduate Diploma in Clinical Embryology starts in 1996. Along with

16

professional clinical development it will offer modules on communication skills, recognizing the valuable part they play in day to day contact with patients and their role as members of a multidisciplinary team.

Counselling Staff

Counsellors come from a variety of backgrounds: social work, nursing, psychology and clerics. Their status within the team was increased with the advent of the HFEA but there has been no clear indication of acceptable training for this important role. In 1995 the HFEA set up a working party to address just this matter and the British Infertility Counselling Association (BICA) and the British Fertility Society (BFS) have agreed, with the help of other interested organizations to take forward the establishing of accredited counselling qualifications appropriate for counsellors in infertility.

Support for the Team Members

The members of the team become very important people in the lives of those for whom they care. Much is invested in their "magical power" of bestowing fertility and there are issues raised by this scenario. Fertility is a personal concern both of professionals and patients and in the close relationships developed with patients during treatment many unexpected areas of concern can arise. Professionals need to set up open dialogue with other members of the team to allow expression of areas of individual concern. During treatment the professional is at risk of being placed in the role of mother or father if the patient adopts a child-like dependence. Expectations are high and may be unrealistic. Cultural differences may place both the patient and the professional in difficult situations and sometimes confrontational attitudes cause problems. The pregnancy of team members may be seen as an insult or a hope that some of the "magic" may brush off on the patients. Staff have concerns about their pregnancy and its effect on those for whom they care and appreciate the support of colleagues in coping with this dilemma. Managing the stress and distress of such an emotional minefield needs attention and recognition within the team.

PRACTICE IN OTHER COUNTRIES

Regulatory bodies in other countries, where they exist, have differing terms of reference and reflect the culture and society they represent.

Regulation

Reproductive practice is in most countries determined by regulation either with a national or local Code of Practice. The power and scope of legal requirements is quite selective: for example, Australian law focuses on screening for viruses in donor gametes and leaves even the licensing of clinics to its Fertility Society. The UK is seen as imposing strict rules on practice, as is Germany, which has forbidden the use of oocyte donation and prohibits the use of embryos in research. The USA is self-regulatory through the American Fertility Society and moreover has State and Federal regulations that influence practice and funding.

Publication of Results

The American Fertility Society has developed specific guidelines to define standards of care offered to infertile couples. By law all clinics must report their pregnancy rates to the Department of Health and Human Services, but as yet they do not have to publish detailed results as in the UK. Swedish clinics report their activities each year by sending their results to the Central Health Authorities.

Age Limits and Social Status

It appears that the application of age criteria for the woman has a relation to the outcome of treatment. Statistically the chances of success decline with age. To this end some countries have adopted an arbitrary age limit for women receiving IVF ranging from 38 years in Norway to 45 years in Singapore. Italy has gained notoriety through its apparent willingness to allow post-menopausal women to have IVF treatment, usually with donor

18

oocytes (Flamigni and Borini 1995, p. 1237). They have a thorough health assessment before undergoing treatment because pregnancy exposes them to a greater risk of maternal complications such as pre-eclampsia, premature labour and instrumental and surgical deliveries (Benshushan and Shenker 1993, p. 321).

Cryopreservation

The Austrian Act on Procreative Medicine allows embryos to be frozen for up to 1 year after which the 'procreative material' must be destroyed (Bernat and Vranes 1993, p. 451). In Sweden, where the same restriction applies, the law states that in 'certain circumstances', which are not defined, application may be made for prolongation of the cryopreservation period (Hamberger and Wikland 1993, p. 244). This contrasts with Australia where embryos may be frozen for up to 10 years, after which local ethical committees decide their fate. These appear to be the two extremes determined by law with countries such as Japan adopting a period of cryopreservation that 'must not exceed the span of marital life of the patient's or the wife's reproductive age' (Mori 1992, p. 296).

Embryo Research

Belief about the status of the human embryo has much to do with prohibiting or allowing embryo research. As already stated in this chapter, debate on this point relates as much to social values and attitudes as to the scientific benefits to be gained from research. Countries have either adopted a total ban or taken a viewpoint as in the UK that a 2 week window from fertilization is acceptable. Differences between countries within the European Convention on Human Rights demonstrate divergent ideological beliefs within what can otherwise be seen as a community without boundaries.

Ovum and Sperm Donation

Any gamete donation is strictly forbidden under the Moslem code, so all Moslem countries forbid ovum donation. An analogous situation arises in Austria where the law states that 'Only oocytes

19

and sperm derived from a married couple or cohabitants may be used for their assisted reproduction'. However, donor sperm may be used *in vivo* 'when the husband's or cohabitant's sperm is not reproductive' (Bernat and Vranes 1993, p. 450). The same regulation applies in Japan even though donor insemination has been used as a treatment option for infertile couples since 1949 (Mori 1992, p. 295). In general a conservative approach is favoured, with some countries applying strict medical criteria about who can donate and who can be the recipients because of the risks of infection and inheritable genetic disease.

Embryo Transfer

The number of embryos transferred in any cycle of treatment has in general fallen since the first days of IVF. The upper limit is left in the hands of the prevailing medical opinion in Austria. Whilst the UK, Germany and Australia elect to replace up to three embryos, USA has no limits by either guidelines or regulation. To reduce the risk of maternal and foetal morbidity associated with a multiple gestation pregnancy, the practice of embryo reduction may be employed, (Maymon 1995, p. 668).

Treatment Reimbursement

Britain is the only country in Europe that does not provide some government help with advanced fertility treatments (Brinsden 1994, p. 806). Information gathered by N.V. Organon (a Dutch health care company) and published in their IVF News 1996 reveals that few countries reimburse infertility treatments either via private health insurance or public health schemes such as the NHS. Most countries have restrictions applied to reimbursement ranging from female age limits and tubal factor infertility only, to number of cycles of treatment. Australia subsidizes up to six cycles without applying restrictive criteria and appears to be the most liberal in this respect.

Religious Influences

The influence of religious ideologies on procreation and infertility changes practice throughout the world. It also has great significance for any multicultural society wanting to offer the most appropriate and up-to-date medical treatment for alleviating the suffering of the infertile. People living in foreign countries will be treated according to the prevailing values of that country and may be either exposed to treatments unacceptable to their own moral code or restricted by the religious differences that exist within that country.

Traditionally the role of procreation has been important in all societies and a "duty to be fruitful and multiply" may lead to embracing assisted conception methods. The Christian view that children should be the result of intercourse within marriage restricts especially Roman Catholics to treatments that do not involve the creation of embryos outside the body (Fryday 1995, p. 31). The Islamic, Jewish and Buddhist religions adopt a more liberal approach recognizing that the pursuit of a remedy for childlessness is legitimate and should be made use of.

Lack of genealogy, inheritance issues and incest all play a part in the acceptance of treatment involving donor gametes. The Greek Orthodox and Roman Catholic churches reject donor insemination as an adulterous act whilst the Hindu view is that if another man's sperm is to be used it should be from another member of the husband's family (Schenker 1992, p. 5). One of the foremost principles in caring for others is not to offend the dignity of the person; it is therefore important to have some understanding of the power of individual belief systems.

UK law will change to reflect evolving clinical practice and cultural views of assisted reproduction. Reviewing current practice in other countries allows for some reflection about how others perceive the problems associated with infertility and the steps they are prepared to take to alleviate suffering.

REFERENCES

Barlow, D.H. (1992) In: Templeton, A.A. and Drife, J.O. (Eds) *Infertility,* London: Springer–Verlag.

Benshushan, A. and Shenker, J.G. (1983) Age limitation in human reproduction: is it justified? *Journal of Assisted Reproduction and Genetics* **10**, 321–331.

Bernat, E. and Vranes, E. (1993) The Austrian Act on Procreative Medicine: scope, impacts and inconsistencies. *Journal of Assisted Reproduction and Genetics* **10**, 449–452.

21

BMA (1996) *Changing Conceptions of Motherhood. The Practice of Surrogacy in Britain*, London: British Medical Association.

Bolton, V.N. and Parsons, J.H. (1991) A tax on infertility? *British Medical Journal* **303**, 309.

Brinsden, P. (1994) 'Tax' on infertility is increased. *British Medical Journal* **309**, 806.

College of Health (1994) *Report of the National Survey of the Funding and Provision of Infertility Services in the United Kingdom*. National Infertility Awareness Campaign London: College of Health.

Flamigni, C. and Borini, A. (1995) Counselling post-menopausal women for donor *in-vitro* fertilisation and hormone replacement therapy. *Human Reproduction* **10**, 1237–1241.

Fryday, M. (1995) Treating infertility in Roman Catholics. *Nursing Standard* **10**, 31–37.

Hamberger, L. and Wikland, M. (1993) Regulations and results concerning assisted reproduction in Sweden. *Journal of Assisted Reproduction and Genetics* **10**, 243–245.

Handyside, A. (1992) In: Templeton, A.A. and Drife, J.O. (Eds) *Infertility*, London: Springer-Verlag, Ch. 22.

Hewitt, J. (1991) A tax on infertility. *British Medical Journal* **303**, 244.

Human Fertilization and Embryology Act (1990) London: HMSO.

Human Fertilization and Embryology Authority (1994) *Third Annual Report*, London: HFEA, p. 21.

Human Fertilization and Embryology Authority (1995a) *Fourth Annual Report*, London: HFEA.

Human Fertilization and Embryology Authority (1995b) *Code of Practice*, London: HFEA.

Human Fertilization and Embryology Authority (1995c) *Patient's Guide to DI and IVF Clinics*, London: HFEA.

King's Fund Centre (1991) *Counselling for Regulated Infertility Treatments*, London: King's Fund Centre.

Leiberman, B.A., Matson, P.L. and Hamer, F. (1994) The UK Human Fertilisation and Embryology Act 1990. How well is it functioning? *Human Reproduction* **9**, 1779–1782.

Morgan, C., Sinclair, L., Sharif, K., Bilalis, D. and Afnan, M. (1996) The effect of structured educational interview on the chosen number of transferred embryos after IVF. *Journal of the British Fertility Society* **1**, no. 1; published as national supplement to *Human Reproduction* **11**, no. 2.

Mori, T. (1992) National regulation of and acheivements in assisted reproduction in Japan. *Journal of Assisted Reproduction and Genetics* **9**, 293–298.

Schenker, J.G. (1992) Religious views regarding treatment of infertility by assisted reproductive technologies. *Journal of Assisted Reproduction and Genetics* **9**, 3–8.

Warnock, M. (1988) *Report of the Committee of Inquiry into Human Fertilisation and Embryology*, Reprint, London: HMSO.

Chapter 2

The Causes, Diagnosis and Medical Treatment of Infertility

Those already working with infertility will have some understanding of the causes of infertility. This chapter offers a brief review of the causes and explores the diagnostic and treatment procedures currently available in England.

Recently, an exhibition at the Natural History Museum was entitled 'The Infertility Maze'. Certainly, entering into the world of finding out about fertility may lead down many unexpected paths and into areas where there may be no definite answers and many possible courses of action. For many, the care they will receive will depend not only on the knowledge and skill of their medical practitioners, but also access to necessary treatments. People who seek medical assistance with infertility should be offered a great deal of information about their options for investigations and treatment. Those who do not receive clear and explicit advice and information are likely to experience greater distress than that arising from their inability to conceive.

FINDING OUT – INVESTIGATIONS, WHAT THE GP CAN DO

The first professional to become involved in this intimate problem will in many cases be a general practitioner (GP). Many couples seek the advice of their GP when first planning to start a family and there are several areas that can be covered with the GP, which, if not directly treating any problem yet to be identified, will help in preparing the couple for pregnancy (Simpson 1995).

Pre-conceptual Advice – Taking Care of Yourself

There has been an increase in the literature available through the Department of Health on maintaining a healthy lifestyle, giving general advice on diet, weight and the use of vitamin supplementation. Recently, a link between folic acid and the reduction of spina bifida has received publicity (Pregnancy, Folic Acid and You, Department of Health October 1993). Booklets such as the Family Planning Infertility Tests and Treatment (published by the Family Planning Association (FPA)) give couples some idea of the reasons why conceiving may be a problem but once again access to this information is determined by the professionals' knowledge of the availability of this kind of literature and its supportive function.

Rubella Screening

Most women will have been given the chance to have rubella immunization during their school days since the advent of the measles, mumps, rubella (MMR) vaccine. There will always be those who did not receive the vaccine and so this is an ideal time to ensure uptake.

Timing of Intercourse

Simple information about the female reproductive system and the menstrual cycle enables couples to increase their chance of conception. Tur-Kaspa *et al.* (1994) suggest that for men with

24

oligo- or asthenospermia, the total motile sperm counts may be increased by having intercourse every day or even twice a day at the time of ovulation, thereby enhancing fertilizing capacity. Recent studies have indicated that the optimum time for intercourse is during a 6-day period ending on the day of ovulation (Simpson 1995, p. 1564; Wilcox 1995, p. 1517).

Predicting Ovulation

Commercial ovulation predictor kits are now widely available and have taken over from the temperature charts used by many. They are expensive to use for every month but are accurate and can be more easily interpreted.

Pre-conceptual advice can be seen as enabling because it allows an individual to take action about his or her fertility and redresses the balance of power, which may be about control. Investigations take time, and waiting for results that may lead to more tests is frustrating and stress-inducing. If the professionals themselves assume a certain level of knowledge about reproduction, they may delay access to appropriate treatment or proceed to unnecessary intervention. Assisted conception is an ever-changing arena and requires specialist knowledge to ensure that appropriate care is offered.

Diagnostic Work-up

Many basic blood tests on the hormonal status of the woman can be completed at this stage to determine an identifiable cause. At present there is a diversity in which tests should be completed for the couple because doctors vary in their approach. Sperm samples will be required for standard microscopy to help determine the fertility status of the man. There should be a physical examination of both partners together with medical and coital history.

It is recommended in *Effective Health Care in Action* (University of Leeds 1992) that clear guidelines about the initial work-up and referral could be arranged with the local specialist infertility centre so that time and money are not wasted by either the individuals seeking care or the service provider. When this is not practical the adoption of guidelines from the Royal College of

Obstetricians and Gynaecologists' *Guidelines for Infertility Practice* (RCOG 1992) would help both the practitioner and the couple ensure thorough work-up before referral. Emslie and Grimshaw (1994, p. 590) demonstrated in their study that 'Management of infertile couples by practices who used guidelines improved in all areas'. The British Fertility Society (BFS) has circulated its members with suggestions for primary care at GP level and specialist practice with the aim of reaching a reliable diagnosis to aid selection of appropriate treatment options and offer prospects of their success. Management at this level can give the GP a key role in speedy identification of those who require referral for specialist care. All through that specialist care there will be dialogue between the specialist and the GP, as many of the treatments involve his/her cooperation in offering support with prescriptions for drugs and administering injections.

Ongoing psychological support at this point can reduce the stress levels of those who need more intervention. Some studies suggest that those who have investigations and treatments over a prolonged period of time without a positive outcome, i.e. a child, have higher anxiety and depression scores suggesting that there is no adaptation to the stress of infertility (Hinton *et al.* 1995, p. 238) whereas others appear to demonstrate that a grief process can be more clearly defined and adaptation takes place during the investigation and treatment process (Baldwin *et al.* 1995, p. 807).

Couples have reported that their first contact with the GP influenced them greatly. For some it was not a happy relationship, as they felt they were not taken seriously or were dealt with insensitively: 'We were initially advised to wait. It was 18 months before any tests were carried out'. Time is an important issue for women, particularly as fertility declines naturally with age. If the GP adopts a wait-and-see policy, inevitably some couples will conceive; a variable spontaneous conception rate can be demonstrated amongst those waiting for and receiving treatment (Collins *et al.* 1983, p. 1205). It is considerably higher for those with the diagnosis of unexplained infertility but 9% of the pregnancies reported had an identifiable clinical cause such as azoospermia and bilateral tubal occlusion. However, many women will not conceive and may then be too old to be accepted for NHS funded assisted conception methods. Availability of further treatment will then depend on the financial resources of the couple.

Family Planning Clinics

Family Planning clinics play a clear and valuable role at the start of investigations. This will of course depend on local provision of service. If they establish links with the infertility service then they may be able to offer their patients a speedier route through investigations, saving both time and resources and duplication of tests. They also have access to support and counselling in the community. For instance, they have contact with groups such as The Miscarriage Association, local infertility support groups and counselling facilities such as psycho-sexual counsellors where appropriate.

MOVING ON – DIAGNOSIS

Human fertility is relatively poor. The average monthly chance of conceiving for couples with proven fertility is around 20–25% (Hull 1992b, p. 34). Subfertility may be defined as the possibility of fertilization occurring whereas a diagnosis of infertility can be given in the presence of complete tubal occlusion, premature menopause or azoospermia. Fertilization in these cases can only take place with the help of medical intervention. However, infertility is the most common term used for both of the above scenarios.

Distribution between primary and secondary infertility has not been clearly defined but secondary infertility is believed to be more common than primary (Hull 1992b, p. 35). Infertility treatment can fully restore fertility and so no further medical assistance is required, as in the case of tubal surgery, or it may only alleviate infertility temporarily. Couples will need to return for treatments to complete the family they wish to have and so the numbers of those with secondary infertility will appear to increase.

CAUSES OF INFERTILITY

A study completed by Hull *et al.* in Bristol 10 years ago is still used to demonstrate the incidence and causes of subfertility and infertility (Table 2.1).

Table 2.1 Causes of infertility

CAUSES	% OF COUPLES (N = 472)
Unexplained	28
Failure of ovulation	21
Tubal damage	14
Endometriosis	6
Sperm defects or dysfunction	24
Oligospermia	15
Azoospermia	6
Coital failure	2

The percentages total more than 100 because some couples had more than one reason for their infertility.

Key elements necessary for conception (Hull *et al.* 1985, p. 785) are:

- ovulation
- egg uptake and passage along the fallopian tubes
- timed coital delivery of sperm
- cervical mucous secretion and receptivity
- sperm motility to penetrate cervical mucus and reach fallopian tubes
- fertilization in the fallopian tubes
- uterine receptivity
- implantation of the embryo.

For those with infertility it may be any one or several of the above reasons why they are not conceiving. Indeed, they may have none of the above and still not conceive spontaneously.

MALE INFERTILITY

This common cause of infertility is probably the least talked of and the least investigated until recently. In the past, male infertility was circumnavigated with the use of donor sperm. This was reasonably accessible to those who required it and its use has been documented from the early 1890s.

There is now much debate about whether male subfertility has increased over the last decade. Reports that sperm counts have decreased in the last 50 years (Auger 1995, p. 281) have led to speculation about whether this has affected male reproductive capacity. Links with environmental causes and oestrogen contamination have been suggested as causative factors. It is certain that there is still a great deal to be learnt about the capacities of sperm. Most analyses depend on subjective rather than objective criteria and it is argued that the studies showing a trend towards decreased fertility were not well controlled (Howards 1995, *et al.* p. 312).

Sperm disorders, defects and dysfunction are the most common reasons for subfertility in men. Assessing the fertilizing capacity of sperm has been open to wide interpretation because there is no absolute agreement on the importance of fluctuations in the accepted parameters. Generally results are based on a subjective evaluation, which may demonstrate differences between laboratories and even individuals. This has become an area of great interest to scientists.

Diagnosis

The most commonly used diagnostic test to assess the level of fertility is a semen analysis in the laboratory. There has been no absolute agreement about the normal levels of the parameters used but there are generally accepted guides. These all make the assumption that any one sample is representative of the individual and that the quality of that sample is static. These assumptions may not be valid, so that a diagnosis for the male may require analysis of more than one sample. Given that all analyses have some element of subjectivity, it is important to repeat the samples at the same laboratory with the same examiner.

Differing parameters of a normal sample are recorded in books that are freely available to the public and may cause some concern if it is not explained that these are a guide and may not reflect the true fertilizing capacity of sperm. For example, the parameters shown in Table 2.2 are listed as 'normal' sperm analyses.

Table 2.2 'Normal' sperm analyses in two publications

PARAMETER	TAN & JACOBS (1991)	NEUBERG (1991)
Volume (ml)	1.5–6.0	$\geqslant 2.0$
Count/density	$\geqslant 20$ million ml^{-1}	> 30 million ml^{-1}
Morphology	$> 60\%$ normal	$< 30\%$ abnormally shaped

There is bound to be confusion for the patient in interpreting these parameters, especially as these differences may not be indicative of how the sperm function when given an egg to fertilize *in vitro*. Much more is now being charted about the behaviour of sperm with the advent of computer assisted techniques, the aim of which is to predict the fertilizing capacity of a given sperm sample (Macleod and Irvine 1995, p. 580).

Semen samples will also undergo microscopic examination for pus cells and a white cell count will demonstrate evidence of infection, which can affect the fertilizing ability of sperm. It may be a non-specific infection or due to the presence of a sexually transmitted disease such as chlamydia.

Oligospermia

This is a reduction in the numbers of sperm produced resulting in a count that is below accepted parameters. This will be of little predictive value for fertilization, and can lead to an incorrect diagnosis being given by those who are not up to date with the latest techniques available for enhancing fertilization.

Azoospermia

This is the absence of any sperm in the seminal fluid under normal microscope analysis but an analysis at any specialized laboratory with greater magnification may identify occasional sperm. For this reason it is essential to repeat analyses when attending a specialist unit. If no sperm can be identified then obstruction or absence of the vas deferens is suspected and a chromosome analysis should be completed to rule out any genetic abnormality.

Obstructions

Congenital absence of the vas deferens, which transports the seminal fluid from the testis to the seminal vesicles, is a rare cause of infertility. It is commonly associated with cystic fibrosis.

Retrograde ejaculation

For some men there will be little or no fluid present at ejaculation because the sperm are being ejaculated into the bladder. It will be possible to identify the presence of sperm in a urine sample. This failure to ejaculate sperm probably results from an obstruction caused by infection or injury. A history of undescended testes as a child and/or sport and back injuries may result in problems with sperm production and transport.

Techniques are now available that retrieve sperm direct from the epididymis by surgically removing the sperm: micro-epididymal sperm aspiration (MESA) and, more recently, percutaneous removal with a small needle (percutaneous epididymal sperm aspiration (PESA)) have been reported (Tsirigotis *et al.* 1995 p. 3) as well as cases where sperm have been retrieved from the testicle in this manner (testicular epididymal sperm aspiration (TESA)). Open microsurgical retrieval of sperm is usually performed under a general anaesthetic because of the surgical exploration of the scrotum.This carries potential complications such as pain, haematoma of the scrotum and infection (Khalifa 1996, p. 5). The percutaneous method, performed under sedation, should reduce the risk of complications. The sperm thus retrieved have been used in conventional *in vitro* fertilization (IVF) and intracytoplasmic sperm injection (ICSI) (Silber *et al.* 1994, p. 1705). In conventional IVF the fertilization rates were poor but with the development of ICSI, fertilization rates have dramatically improved (as above).

31

Hormonal disorders

An endocrine assessment may be necessary to eliminate hormonal imbalance such as follicle-stimulating hormone (FSH), luteinizing hormone (LH) and testosterone levels. Those with gonadotrophin deficiency respond well to treatment with human FSH and LH or human chorionic gonadotrophin. This therapy has been shown to increase the chance of conception (Skakkeback *et al.* 1994, p. 1479).

Antibody problems

On examination, sperm will be seen to clump together and so reduce their individual chance of fertilizing eggs. Sperm washing and the use of intrauterine insemination (IUI) have been of some help in enabling otherwise healthy sperm to fertilize eggs.

Treatments

There has been little on offer to men whose sperm samples vary from the generally accepted 'normal' parameters until the development of assisted fertilization procedures aimed at assisting the passage of sperm into the oocyte: partial zonal dissection (PZD) and subzonal insemination (SUZI). These techniques were employed to help in cases of poor sperm morphology. Pregnancies and births are reported from these methods but there are still many failed fertilizations (Tarin 1995, p. 168).

Pentoxifylline has been used to stimulate sperm in cases of poor motility but whether this is of great clinical significance in enhancing fertilization is still being debated (Yovich *et al.* 1990, p. 715; Kay *et al.* 1993, p. 727; Tournaye *et al.* 1993, p. 210; Dimitriadou *et al.* 1995, p. 880).

In 1992 a new method was reported in which a single spermatazoon is injected into the oocyte (Palermo *et al.* 1992, p. 17), called intracytoplasmic sperm injection (ICSI). Since then the same group has reported on 1275 ICSI cycles with a 60% rate of micro-injected oocytes with normal fertilization. The pregnancy rate is around 30%. This method produces fertilization and pregnancies in couples who have previously had failed fertilization, impaired semen parameters or where sperm retrieval techniques were used. This has changed considerably the boundaries for men who would have previously been directed to using donor sperm to help them to achieve a pregnancy. Since the advent of ICSI the use of SUZI has decreased because of the higher number of embryos available for transfer, resulting in a higher pregnancy rate associated with ICSI (Abdalla 1995, p. 2944). Research is now in progress looking at the fertilizing capacity of spermatids, which are the immature sperm found in ejaculates produced both by masturbation and in surgically retrieved samples. Indeed, with the advent of the use of spermatids there is hope for those with very poor sperm quality. A continuing pregnancy was reported in 1995 (Fishel *et al.* 1995, p. 1641) although little is yet known about the possible hazards of using these immature cells in humans and the safety of this method of treatment.

Questions about whether these micromanipulative procedures increase the risk of genetic disorders, either as a risk of the procedure or because of an underlying genetic pathology that may be a cause of the infertility, have been studied by a team of geneticists, and they conclude that whilst initially there seems to be no cause for concern (Bonduelle *et al.* 1995, p. 3327), there is not a large enough database on the long-term development of children born after ICSI on which to base a decision (Meschede *et al.* 1995, p. 2884).

All of the above methods rely on the female undergoing stimulation of her ovaries with drugs and oocyte recovery for IVF.

FEMALE INFERTILITY

Ovulation Problems

The following groups can be recognized as having some ovulatory dysfunction. There is a spectrum of conditions between normal ovulation and total anovulation. Ovulation may occur irregularly and cannot be predicted, only confirmed after the event. In all cases there will be some disturbance in the function of the hypothalamic–pituitary–ovarian axis that may be persistent enough to lead to treatment. Endocrine assessments may be normal or abnormal and normal fertility can be restored by lifestyle changes such as increasing or losing weight and avoiding over-exercising, where appropriate.

Investigations will include assessment of serum FSH, LH, day 21 progesterone, prolactin level and thyroid stimulating hormone (TSH). The range of findings will include the following:

Normal FSH, LH and prolactin levels are suggestive of disordered ovulation which can be corrected.

Raised FSH levels are suggestive of primary or premature ovarian failure. If this is persistent there is no treatment that can induce the ovaries to function (Crosignani *et al.* 1995, p. 1549) but with oocyte donation a pregnancy can be achieved.

Raised LH levels are suggestive of polycystic ovaries (PCO), which in themselves may not constitute a problem but may be indicative of polycystic ovarian disease.

Hyperprolactinaemia has been identified as disrupting the normal menstrual cycle but its exact role in infertility has not been fully elucidated (Peperell and O'Herlihy 1985, p. 516). The condition is associated with pituitary adenomas and hypothyroidism and these causes must be investigated. If necessary treatment to reduce the levels needs to be instituted when fertility treatment is initiated.

Polycystic ovarian disease (PCOD), sometimes called polycystic ovarian syndrome (PCOS), may be the most common cause of anovulatory infertility. Since the advent of real-time ultrasound scanning it has become apparent that cysts on the ovaries are common, but this in itself is not indicative of a disease or syndrome (Clayton *et al.* 1992, p. 127). However, if the ovary has 10 or more cysts, 2–8 mm in diameter, arranged around an echo-dense central stroma, then PCOD is suspected. Indeed, Hull (1989, p. 21) concluded that vaginal or abdominal ultrasonography of the ovaries gave a positive diagnosis in 95% of cases, and with the development of expertise in ultrasonography, more clinicians are using this method of diagnosis. The most common factors associated with PCOS – raised serum LH, hyperandrogenism, obesity and menstrual irregularities – are not all present in every case.

Treatment for anovulation

If possible, the underlying cause should be treated, e.g. in the presence of hyperprolactinaemia, bromocriptine therapy restores normal ovulation, and weight loss for those with PCOS is often followed by the return of normal ovulatory cycles. In the absence of normal ovulatory cycles the first-line treatment of choice will be medical induction of ovulation. This will be discussed later in this chapter.

Endometriosis

Whilst endometriosis is implicated in fertility problems, its cause is as yet unknown. The disease occurs when endometrial cells grow outside the uterus. In many cases these cells are found in or around the ovaries, fallopian tubes or indeed anywhere in the peritoneum. The series of events leading to this condition is still under investigation but the fact that it can be seen in lungs, skeletal muscle, the subarachnoid space and kidneys indicates that investigations of the properties of the endometrial cells are required. One theory is that retrograde flow of endometrial cells occurs during menstruation and implantation results in endometriosis. The extent of the disease is difficult to assess medically as some women are asymptomatic and diagnosis will be made at laparoscopy when the distinctive lesions can be visualized. Others will present initially with pelvic pain that is severe before and after menstruation. This may be unrelated to fertility events but it is at this point that the possibility of infertility is raised. The degree of the symptoms is not related to the severity of the disease, i.e. those with no symptoms may have severe endometriotic lesions which threaten their fertility.

Diagnosis can usually be made at laparoscopy where evidence of the spread of endometrial cells can be seen. Cysts on the ovaries may also contain chocolate-coloured fluid, evidence of the presence of endometriotic cells. Non-pigmented lesions have been found on histological examination and can indicate that it may be difficult to assess the full extent of disease. The extent of the damage can be mild to severe and has been classified by the American Fertility Society (1985).

Endometriosis can compromise fertility by causing damage,

35

in the form of adhesions, and distortion to the pelvic anatomy. Unfortunately, this is not always quantifiable and together with the findings that the shorter the period of infertility, the greater the successful outcome (Lelaidier *et al.* 1993, p. 432), treating the condition within the context of infertility demands great skill. There is a clear need for early diagnosis and prompt treatment.

Treatment for endometriosis

There are three accepted approaches to treating endometriosis:

- *Expectant management* or the 'do nothing' approach. If there are no symptoms and the laparoscopy shows grade 1 or 2 disease then fertility may not be jeopardized and adopting a 6–12 month wait after diagnosis may result in a spontaneous pregnancy rate that is not significantly different from the rate in those receiving medical therapy (Hull *et al.* 1987, p. 44). If a fertility problem still persists, medical or surgical treatment is then recommended (Healy *et al.* 1994, p. 1540).
- *Medical.* The disease is known to be oestrogen dependent. Treatment is aimed at suppressing the cyclical hormonal changes. Gonadotrophin-releasing hormone (GnRH) agonists such as nafarelin and buserelin have been shown to have a significant impact on the disease process and effectively induce a hypo-oestrogenic state (Sandow 1983, p. 571). This means the cessation of a normal menstrual cycle but delays the progress of the disease so that after a treatment phase normal fertility may be restored. Danazol has been used to treat endometriosis for over a decade and is still the main drug used to treat the disease. In offering medical therapy for this disease, symptoms will be alleviated and lesions may be reduced but fertility may not be improved and surgery may be required before assisting conception with IVF.
- *Surgical.* Superficial implants can be treated by coagulation using the CO_2 laser. Vaporization and excision of deep and fibrotic implants is valuable but laparoscopic stripping of ovarian endometrioma is quicker and has been described as the treatment of choice (Martin 1991, p. 459). Problems with any treatment of endometriosis are that the condition reoccurs

after treatment. IVF techniques that use GnRH agonists are beneficial to patients with endometriosis at any stage of the disease. However, although some groups report pregnancy rates lower than in a group with tubal disease (Wardle *et al.* 1985, p. 236), a recent study has found comparable pregnancy rates (Dmowski *et al.* 1995, p. 555) and certainly endometriosis is given as a reason for IVF treatment in 9% of cycles related to female infertility reported to the Human Fertilization and Embryology Authority (HFEA) in 1992 (HFEA 1994).

Tubal Infertility

Pelvic inflammatory disease accounts for many cases of female infertility. Pelvic surgery, endometriosis, ruptured appendix and coil contraception can all result in degrees of tubal damage. *Chlamydia* is now the most common causative organism with gonococcal infection having reduced in western society. Screening for *Chlamydia* should form part of the early diagnostic work-up. The infertility risks are reported to double with increased episodes of infection (Healy *et al.* 1994, p. 1539).

Treatment

Successful surgery depends on the extent and site of occlusion and the skill of the surgeon. The decision by commissioning health authorities to purchase tubal microsurgery varies throughout the UK, affecting provision within the NHS. Success rates vary and in many cases IVF is offered as a more successful option. *Effective Health Care in Action* recommended that resources could be devoted to identifying correctly those for whom the surgical technique will be of more benefit than IVF (University of Leeds 1992).

Easy access to female sterilization has resulted in many women seeking reversal after divorce and the establishment of a new relationship. Recently, a trend away from offering reversal of sterilization has resulted in more couples coming for IVF although a recent study from France concluded that microsurgical repermeabilization is the first-choice treatment, offering higher pregnancy rates than IVF (Dubuisson *et al.* 1995, p. 1145).

37

The decision as to whether women receive treatment or not within the NHS may now rest outside the clinical arena.

Uterine Factor

The role of the endometrium in aiding implantation is currently under review. With the advent of colour Doppler ultrasonography, the receptivity of the endometrial lining can be assessed (Tan & Jacobs 1991, p. 42). Fibroids and other uterine abnormalities are known to have a relationship with infertility but may have more influence on implantation, a subject that is difficult to investigate in humans because of the risk of interfering with the natural processes involved.

Cervical Factor

Investigations may reveal poor production of mucus, anatomical abnormalities or hostile mucus. These factors can prevent sperm from reaching the ovum. First it is important to address the problem. If physical, the problem should be corrected if possible, i.e. female anatomy not allowing penetration may require surgical intervention to allow sexual intercourse to take place. The male partner may need circumcision. Careful discussion about sexual intercourse with the couple may reveal psychological issues that require the skills of a psychosexual therapist. If having identified and treated appropriately any findings and still no pregnancy occurs then the couple will move on to fertility treatment.

UNEXPLAINED INFERTILITY

Unexplained or undiagnosed infertility accounts for 28% of all infertility. This conclusion is arrived at after a lengthy and extensive investigative period and is really a negative diagnosis. All the hormonal and physical investigations will be within normal limits and, in the absence of a firm reason, the couple will be left with more questions than medicine can as yet answer. This is a difficult situation for many to handle and is an unsatisfactory label to deal with emotionally. If it is a fact that the longer the infertility the smaller the chances are of having a child, then couples given this unsatisfactory non-diagnosis will have been undergoing tests and investigations for around 2 years and the woman's age may decrease her chances of success. The literature reporting on unexplained infertility seems to suggest that initially a spontaneous pregnancy may occur because many of the couples have normal fertility but have not been 'lucky'. (Hull 1992b, p. 48) and it is suggested that Clomid, IUI and GIFT/IVF should be offered only when the woman is in her late 30s or the infertility is prolonged (over 3 years).

WHAT'S NEXT – TREATMENT TECHNIQUES

Induction of Ovulation

Clomiphene citrate

If ovulation is in question, some GPs choose to initiate induction of ovulation whilst waiting for referral. Empirical use of clomiphene and/or tamoxifen, the most common drugs, without adequate monitoring by serial ultrasound measurements during one cycle or day 21 progesterone assays is not recommended.

Clomiphene can successfully induce ovulation in women with mild to moderate hypothalamic disorders, including those with PCOs. It is probably one of the easiest and most cost-effective treatments available. It is an oral active non-steroidal compound that increases gonadotrophin release. This in turn promotes pre-ovulatory follicular formation (Peperell and O'Herlihy 1985, p. 511). Tamoxifen has also been used with the same effect (Crosignani and Rubin 1995). Prescribing empirically without knowledge or monitoring of the woman's ovulatory status may result in multiple folliculargenesis and subsequent risk of multiple pregnancy. Peperell and O'Herlihy (1985, p. 513) find mid-luteal phase measurements of progesterone valuable in diagnosing an ovulatory result following administration of clomiphene and tamoxifen. In order to avoid overstimulation, monitoring with ultrasonography for at least one cycle will demonstrate ovarian response and help to determine the effectiveness of this mode of treatment for the individual (Healy *et al.* 1994, p. 1542).

A recent study demonstrated an increased risk of ovarian tumours associated with prolonged use of clomiphene, i.e. over 12 cycles (Rossing *et al.* 1994, p. 776). Whilst clomiphene clearly is effective initially, its continued use for over 6 months is debatable (Hull 1992b, p. 49) and if ovulation and/or pregnancy has not been established then gonadotrophin therapy with or without GnRH agonists is indicated.

Concern over the information given to those undertaking ovulation induction about the risks of multiple births was raised in the Study of Triplets and Higher Order Births (Botting *et al.* 1990, p. 57). Mothers who reported having clomiphene prescribed by their GP were not given sufficient information about the risks of multiple pregnancy and these women had conceived three or four babies. Information given before conception is achieved would result in individuals being able to make an informed choice. This kind of information is mandatory in clinics where gametes are being handled, but as the remit of the HFEA does not extend to clinics where drugs are used to stimulate ovulation without proceeding to the use of donor sperm, GIFT or IVF, the information may not be readily available.

Side-effects of this therapy can be unpleasant and include hot flushes, visual disturbances, nausea and vomiting, ovarian enlargement and, rarely, severe forms of hyperstimulation with cyst formation and ascites (Peperell and O'Herlihy 1985, p. 513). The latter are rare when adequate clinical supervision is maintained.

Gonadotrophins

Treatment with human menopausal gonadotrophins (hMG, pure FSH) to stimulate the ovaries, and human chorionic gonadotrophin (hCG) to achieve ovulation, is the next option for those who fail to respond to clomiphene. These drugs have been developed and refined over the years and recently recombinant human FSH has been synthesized in a mammalian cell line. Early research supports the safety and efficacy of this drug in clinical use (Hedon *et al.* 1995, p. 3102; Strowitzki 1995, p. 3097) and it will soon be available in clinics.

Parenteral induction of ovulation (PIO) regimes are varied

and more complicated involving daily subcutaneous or intra-muscular injections, serial blood tests to monitor the rise of oestrogen, and ultrasound screening to assess follicular growth. The aim is to evoke an ovarian response and trigger ovulation. In order to reduce the risks of multiple ovulation and overstimulation of the ovaries, fertility clinics should have defined criteria above which hCG will not be administered (Lunenfeld *et al.* 1985, p. 527). If the response is within normal limits then hCG will be administered and the couple advised of the appropriate timing for intercourse. Analysis of success rates for this treatment is complicated by many variables. Different regimes may be used by the same couple, cycles may be abandoned because of under- or over-response and the age of the female at the time of treatment can vary considerably. Overall, figures are quoted as cumulative pregnancy rates: after nine cycles of treatment, 80.6–81.2%, with a 13% twinning and 3% triplet rate (Healy *et al.* 1994, p. 1542), 91.2% after six cycles (Lunenfeld *et al.* 1985, p. 527) and 62.4–85.3% after 12 cycles (Balen *et al.* 1994, p. 1563).

The addition of IUI of sperm to PIO has added another dimension to this method of treatment. The only exclusion criterion for this treatment is the presence of bilateral tubal damage resulting in non-patent fallopian tubes. Because PIO and IUI are less expensive than other assisted conception techniques, it is often the treatment of choice outside the assisted conception clinics and consequently is more widely available at infertility clinics in District General Hospitals. This method of treatment may be used when semen parameters are reduced, and the use of donor sperm seems to be associated with a higher success rate.

Three to six cycles can be offered depending on the outcome before IVF or gamete intra-fallopian transfer (GIFT) is suggested. Success rates are reported to be generally around 10–12% per cycle with partner sperm but up to 20% with donor sperm. For many, this treatment is the only one acceptable to them as they would not contemplate further techniques, but availability within the NHS is limited and variable and there are no published data, as in IVF, to help couples to make informed choices about which clinic to choose. There are multiple variables associated with this technique. In a comprehensive review of the literature, Martinez *et al.* (1993) suggested that the indications for treatment are multifactorial in approximately one-third of couples treated: treatment regimens differ in terms of cycle stimulation, sperm preparation, insemination timing and technique, and the number of cycles offered.

When PIO is unsuccessful the next step would be to use the more invasive procedures of GIFT, zygote intra-fallopian transfer (ZIFT) or IVF. Clinics vary on the stimulation regimes they use. Many will choose to down-regulate the pituitary hormones using GHRH agonists such as buserelin or Synarel and when the pituitary is suppressed stimulate the ovaries into multiple folliculargenesis with either hMG or FSH. During the stimulation, monitoring is carried out using ultrasound scans and serum oestradiol measurements. Each clinic will differ slightly in the protocol used but the theme remains the same. When the follicles have grown in size to around 17–20 mm, hCG is given to induce ovulation and approximately 36 hours later the oocytes will be harvested either at laparoscopy for GIFT or transvaginal ultrasound-directed follicle aspiration (UDFA) for ZIFT and IVF.

GIFT involves retrieving oocytes from the ovary at laparoscopy and placing the oocytes sequentially with sperm into the woman's fallopian tubes. Those suitable would include women with unexplained infertility, women who have at least one patent and healthy tube, and men whose semen parameters are not reduced.

There are no nationally collated statistics for this technique because it falls outside the remit of the HFEA unless donated oocytes or sperm are used. However, the Code of Practice does state that only three oocytes may be transferred in one treatment cycle. The effectiveness of this treatment has been compared with IVF/embryo transfer (IVF-ET) (Tanbo 1990; Mills *et al.* 1992), and in clinics where IVF-ET is also practised success rates are said to be as good (Hull 1985). If the fertilizing ability of sperm is in question, IVF-ET will be the treatment option as GIFT cannot confirm fertilization unless a pregnancy is established. GIFT centres may be established within District General Hospitals. They do not require IVF laboratory facilities; however, the concurrent *in vitro* fertilization of excess oocytes with sperm can provide information on the fertilizing capacity of the gametes and, of course, if acceptable the resulting embryos can be cryopreserved and transferred in a later cycle.

ZIFT uses the same procedures as IVF up to and including UDFA, but after the pronuclei are seen the day after fertilization the zygotes are transferred at laparoscopy into the midampullary region of the fallopian tube. Several studies have not demonstrated a statistically higher pregnancy rate compared with IVF (Freidler *et al.* 1993, p. 399).

IVF-ET is often viewed as the end of the line treatment for infertile couples. It was initially envisaged as a treatment for women with damaged fallopian tubes but is now a method of choice for all causes of infertility. Following the regimes outlined above, ooctyes are retrieved by aspirating the follicles on the ovary, usually vaginally, then sperm and oocytes are incubated and fertilization takes place *in vitro*. The resulting embryos are transferred to the uterus usually 2 days later.

Problems associated with embryo transfer may play a part in inhibiting implantation. Bleeding permits blood cells to coat the embryo, and cervical manipulation resulting in uterine contractions and release of prostaglandins may play a part. Many of the ectopic pregnancies associated with IVF may occur because the contractions propel the embryos into the fallopian tubes (Freidler 1995, p. 393). Implantation is assisted by the use of progesterone during the 2 weeks after embryo transfer or GIFT/ZIFT. One of two things will occur: either the woman will start to bleed, which will mean the embryos have not implanted, or a pregnancy test 14 days after transfer will be positive. Very rarely, no bleeding starts before the 14th day but a pregnancy test is negative and bleeding usually commences within a few days.

At present the HFEA has licensed 68 centres offering IVF treatment and the success rates are published each year. Their aim is to 'provide people with information which is both meaningful to them and fair to the centres' (HFEA 1994, p. 5). Unfortunately, only a few centres are funded by the NHS so many couples will be seeking care in the private sector.

Complications – Ovarian Hyperstimulation Syndrome

Ovarian hyperstimulation syndrome (OHSS) is an iatrogenic complication of induction of ovulation that can occur with any of the clomiphene and hMG therapies. If not managed appropriately there is rapid deterioration and in its severe form it can be life-threatening. There is a spectrum of degree of severity not always identifiable by the size of the ovarian enlargement.

OHSS can be classified as:

- *mild* with abdominal bloating, heaviness, tension, swelling and mild pain
- *moderate* with the above accompanied by nausea and vomiting. There may be ultrasound evidence of ascites and enlarged ovaries
- *severe* with clinical ascites, haemoconcentration, increased blood viscosity and hypovolaemia. Often hypoproteinaemia, electrolyte disturbance and decreased renal perfusion. Ovaries are greater than 12 cm in diameter.

In moderate to severe cases hospitalization is necessary and treatment is aimed at correcting the fluid balance, relieving the pain and draining the ascites to relieve the tension. Recovery takes around a week but may be prolonged if a pregnancy is established. As the condition is dependent on the administration of hCG, this may be withheld and the treatment cycle, be it IUI or IVF, abandoned.

Attempts have been made to identify those particularly at risk, and before women embark on infertility treatments they should be fully informed of their relative risk and the symptoms they could expect. OHSS has been noted to occur more frequently in conception cycles (Jenkins *et al.* 1995, p. 3).

Multiple Pregnancy

Over the last few years the issue of how many embryos should be replaced at one time has been a matter of great debate. The HFEA has stated that three should be the maximum. In many clinics couples, having thought about the implications of conceiving triplets, decide to have only two transferred. When the professionals involved were asked about the limit of three embryos, most felt that whilst the upper limit was correct, they would be in favour of transferring two embryos in younger women and a minority wanted to reserve an option of four in women over 40 years of age (Leiberman *et al.* 1994, p. 1781). The transfer of two good quality embryos does not appear to reduce significantly the pregnancy rate (Staessen *et al.* 1995, p. 3305) and may avoid unwanted multiple births. The trend towards transferring fewer embryos may also have been influenced by improved cryopreservation techniques and success rates.

Couples achieving multiple births through assisted conception techniques express a desire to have one child at a time. Having twins, triplets or more, demands different parenting skills and once again marks them out as different.

Success Rates

In 1995 the HFEA published *The Patient Guide to DI and IVF Clinics*. Included in this publication are the live birth rates from the treatments carried out between 1 April 1993 and 31 March 1994 for each licensed clinic. This is the first time that the figures for individual clinics have been reported with the live birth rates being adjusted for:

- age of the woman treated
- male factor infertility
- whether the couple have had previous pregnancies
- whether the couple have had previous unsuccessful treatment cycles
- whether fresh or frozen embryos have been used.

By adjusting the records of each clinic to take into account the above factors, the HFEA allows for a direct comparison to be made between the clinics with two provisos:

(1) that it does not reflect the individual couple's chance of a live baby, and
(2) there can be other factors important to each individual which would help them choose a clinic.

Variations

Transport IVF

Some District General Hospitals (DGH) and Private Hospitals have started to offer transport IVF. In most instances all stages up to and including oocyte retrieval are completed at the DGH (satellite centre). The follicle fluids are then transferred by the male partner to the embryology laboratory at the Central IVF Unit for ooctye identification. IVF is then performed and, in cases of severe male factor infertility, ICSI may be performed to achieve fertilization. In some programmes the resulting embryos are transferred back to the satellite centre for replacement (Anyaegbunam *et al.* 1995, p. 18) or the woman attends the central IVF unit for embryo replacement (Booker *et al.* 1993, p. S112). Transport IVF enables couples to benefit from continuity of local care whilst providing them with access to embryological expertise at an established assisted conception unit.

Natural cycle IVF

The early IVF successes resulted from natural cycles. The use of controlled cycles and spare embryo cryopreservation now enables more choice in the timing of oocyte retrieval and natural cycles have only received the attention of a dedicated few. Some units report experiences using hCG to replace and precede the natural LH surge to enable timing of oocyte retrieval (Paulson *et al.* 1994, p. 1572) and others rely on determining the correct timing for oocyte collection by detecting the LH surge from blood samples (Fahy *et al.* 1995, p. 573). Both units conclude that there is benefit in offering natural cycle IVF, especially to women under 40 years of age and with a diagnosis of tubal damage.

Replacement of cryopreserved embryos

When GIFT or IVF treatment results in supernumerary good grade embryos then they may be cryopreserved for use in a later cycle. Again each clinic will differ slightly in both the criteria and methods used in the freezing process and also in whether the embryos are replaced in stimulated or natural cycles. The overall success rates from frozen embryo replacement are quoted as being 12.7% (HFEA 1995, p. 46).

Donor gametes

The donor gamete most often used is undoubtedly sperm. Donors are screened for any genetic risk, infection, HIV, hepatitis B and toxoplasmosis. Social and medical histories are taken and counselling is offered to consider the implications of donating their sperm. Some clinics are licensed specifically for the use of donor sperm and they have to publish their success rates per treatment cycle. Donor insemination (DI) treatment may be carried out in natural cycles or PIO cycles depending on the clinic. The chances of having a baby ranges from 5.1% to 7.4% per cycle and is calculated to be more than 15 cycles (HFEA 1995, p. 46).

Oocyte donors are required to undergo the same stimulation as an IVF cycle and have the ooctyes retrieved at UDFA. The age limit is set at 35 years as the risks of abnormalities, especially Down's syndrome, increases with age. Donors are at risk of hyperstimulation and need full and detailed information about this before they start. They will have the same screening tests as the men. Women may donate their oocytes in exchange for treatment services or sterilization and sometimes women who are themselves undergoing IVF feel able to offer their oocytes if many are retrieved. There are no nationally collated success rates available for this treatment.

Embryos may be donated by a couple who have excess embryos to their requirements during their IVF cycle if they have given their informed consent. With the advent of cryopreservation procedures it seems less likely that there will be embryos to donate.

Surrogacy

Surrogacy that is dependent on IVF may be carried out at IVF clinics with strict criteria and protocols. It is the commissioning woman who will be stimulated to produce oocytes. They will then be fertilized by her partner's sperm or donor sperm. At this stage they may be cryopreserved for transfer to the surrogate at a later date, or they may be transferred at the usual time, which is day 2 or 3 after UDFA.

Assisted conception has come a long way since the first IVF baby. Techniques to improve and enhance conception are constantly on the move. This may make it difficult for those not working in the specialty to keep abreast of developments. The media often report the latest new techniques but as they are often still at the research stage they may raise the hopes of those who would derive benefit from them.

REFERENCES

Abdalla, H., Leonard, T., Pryor, J. and Everett, D. (1995) Comparison of SUZI and ICSI for severe male factor. *Human Reproduction.* **10**, 2941–2944.

American Fertility Society (1985) Revised American Fertility Society classification of endometriosis. *Fertility and Sterility* **43**, 351–354.

Anyaegbunam, W., Biljan, M.M., Barker, E. *et al.* (1995) Comparison between success rates in traditional assisted conception procedures and transport intracytoplasmic injection (T-ICSI). In: *Abstracts of the Annual Conference of the BFS*, Liverpool, p. 18.

Auger, J., Kunstmann, J.M., Czyglik, F. and Jouannet, P. (1995) Decline in semen quality among fertile men in Paris during the past 20 years. *New England Journal of Medicine* **332**, 281–285.

Baldwin, J., Takefman, J.E., Tulandi, T. *et al.* (1995) Reactions to infertility based on extent of treatment failure. *Fertility and Sterility* **63**, 801–807.

Balen, A., Braat, D.D.M., West, C. *et al.* (1994) Cumulative conception and live birth rates after the treatment of anovulatory infertility: safety and efficacy of ovulation induction in 200 patients. *Human Reproduction* **9**, 1563–1570.

Bonduelle, M., Legain, J., Derde, M-P. *et al.* (1995) Comparative follow up study of 130 children born after intracytoplasmic sperm injection and 130 children born after in-vitro fertilization. *Human Reproduction* **10**, 3327–3331.

Booker, M.W., Tucker, J., Hewitt, D. *et al.* (1993) Transport IVF and embryo transfer. In: Abstracts of The American Fertility Society, Birmingham, Alabama: American Fertility Society.

Botting, B.J., Macfarlane, A.J. and Price, F.V. (Eds) (1990) *Three, Four and More Study of Triplets and Higher Order Births*, London: HMSO.

Clayton, R.N., Ogden V., Hodgkinson, J. *et al* (1992) How common are polycystic ovaries and what is their significance for the fertility of the population? *Clinical Endocrinology* **37**, 127–134.

Collins, J.A., Wrixon, W., Janes, L.B. and Wilson, E.H. (1983) Treatment independent pregnancy among infertile couples. *New England Journal of Medicine* **309**, 1201–1205.

Crosignani, P.G. and Rubin, B.L. (1995) The ESHRE Capri Workshop Group on Anovulatory Infertility. *Human Reproduction* **10**, 1549–1553.

Dimitriadou, F., Rizos, D., Mantzavinos, T. *et al.* (1995) The effect of pentoxifylline on sperm motility, oocyte ferilisation, embryo quality, and pregnancy outcome in an *in-vitro* fertilisation program. *Fertility and Sterility* **63** 880–886.

Dmowski, W.P., Rana, N., Michalowska, J., Friberg, J., Papierniak, C. and El-Roeiy, A. (1995) The effect of endometriosis, its stage and activity, and of autoantibodies on *in vitro* fertilisation and embryo transfer success rates. *Fertility and Sterility* **63**, 555–562.

Dubuisson, J-B., Chapron, C. Nos, C., Morice, P., Aubriot F-X. and Garnier, P. (1995) Sterilization reversal: fertility results. *Human Reproduction* **10**, 1145–1151.

Emslie, C. and Grimshaw, J. (1994) Managing infertility – the GPs' role. *The Practioner* **238**, 586–590.

Fahy, U.M., Cahill, D.J., Wardle, P.G. and Hull, M.G.R. (1995) *In vitro* fertilization in completely natural cycles. *Human Reproduction* **10**, 572–575.

Fishel, S., Green, S., Bishop, M. *et al.* (1995) Pregnancy after intracytoplasmic injection of spermatid. *Lancet* **345**, 1641–1642.

Freidler, S., Lewin, A. and Schenker, J.G. (1993) Methology of human embryo transfer following assisted reproduction. *Journal of Assisted Reproduction and Genetics* **10**, 393–404.

Healy, D.L., Trounson, A.O. and Anderson, A.N. (1994) Female infertility: causes and treatment. *Lancet* **343**, 1539–1544.

Hedon, B., Out, H.J., Hughes, J.N. *et al.* (1995) Efficacy and safety of recombinant follicle stimulating hormone (Puregon) in infertile women pituitary suppressed with triptorelin undergoing *in vitro* fertilisation: a prospective, randomized, assessor blind, multicentre trial. *Human Reproduction* **10**, 3102– -3106.

HFEA (1994) *Third Annual Report*, London: HFEA, p. 5.

HFEA (1995a) *Fourth Annual Report*, London: HFEA, p. 46.

HFEA (1995b) *The Patient Guide to DI and IVF Clinics*, London: HFEA.

Hinton, R., Meadoncroft, J. and Wardle, P. (1995) Psychological distress and subfertility. *Journal of the Royal Society of Medicine* **88**, 237–238.

Howards, S.S. (1995) Treatment of male infertility. *New England Journal of Medicine* **332**, 312–317.

Hull, M.G.R. (1989) Polycystic ovarian disease: clinical aspects and prevalence. In: *Research and Clinical Forums*, vol. 11, no. 4, *Current Understanding of Polycystic Ovarian Disease*, England: Royal Wells Press, p. 21.

Hull, M.G.R. (1992a) Infertility treatment, relative effectiveness of conventional and assisted conception methods. *Human Reproduction* **7**, 785.

Hull, M.G.R. (1992b) In: Templeton, A.A. and Drife, J.O. (Eds) *Infertility*, Ch. 3 London: Springer-Verlag, pp. 33–62.

Hull, M.G.R. (1985), Glazener, C.M., Kelly N.J. *et al.* (1985) Population study of causes, treatment, and outcome of fertility. *British Medical Journal* **291**, 1693–1697.

Hull, M.E., Moghissi, K.S., Magyar, D.F. and Hayes, M.F. (1987) Comparison of different treatment modalities of endometriosis in infertile women. *Fertility and Sterility* **47**, 40–44.

Jenkins, J.M., Methur, R.S. and Cooke, I.D. (1995) The management of severe ovarian hyperstimulation syndrome. *British Journal of Obstetrics and Gynaecology* **102**, 2–50.

Khalifa, Y. and Grudzinskas, J.G. (1996) Minimally invasive surgery for male subfertility. *British Medical Journal* **312**, 5.

Kay, V.J., Coutts, J.R.T. and Robertson, J. (1983) Pentoxifylline stimulates hyperactivation in human spermatazoa. *Human Reproduction* 8, 727–731.

Leiberman, B.A., Matson, P.L. and Hamer, F. (1994) The UK Human Fertilisation and Embryology Act 1990: how well is it functioning? *Human Reproduction* 9, 1779–1782.

Lelaidier, C., Caetano J.P.J. and Frydman, R. (1993) *In vitro* fertilisation and endometriosis. In: Brosens, I. and Donnez, J. (Eds) *The Current Status of Endometriosis Research and Management*, Ch. 34, Carnforth, Lancs: Parthenon, p. 432.

Lunenfeld, B., Mashiach, S. and Blankstein, J. (1985) Induction of ovulation with gonadotrophins. In: *Clinical Reproductive Endocrinology*, Ch. 27, Edinburgh: Churchill Livingstone, pp. 523–533.

Macleod, I.C. and Irvine, T.D.S. (1995) The predictive value of computer assisted semen analysis in the context of a donor insemination programme. *Human Reproduction* 10, 580–586.

Martin, D.D. (1991) Laparoscopic treatment of ovarian endometriomas *Clinical Obstetrics and Gynaecology* 34, 452–459.

Martinez, A.R., Bernardos, R.E., Vermeiden, J.P. and Schoemaker, J. (1993) Basic questions on intrauterine insemination: an update. *Obstetrical and Gynaecological Survey* 48, 811–828.

Meschede, D., DeGeyter, C., Nieschlag, E. and Horst, J. (1995) Genetic risk in micromanipulative assisted reproduction. *Human Reproduction* 10, 2880–2886.

Mills, M.S., Eddowes, H.A., Cahill, D.J. *et al.* (1992) A prospective controlled study of *in vitro* fertilisation, gamete intra-fallopian transfer and intra-uterine insemination combined with superovulation. *Human Reproduction* 7, 490–495.

Neuberg, R. (1991) *Infertility*, London: Thorsons, p. 44.

Palermo, G., Joris, H., Devreoy, P., and Van Steirtegheim, A.C. (1992) Pregnancies after intracytoplasmic injection of single spermatazoon into an oocyte. *Lancet* 340, 17–18.

Paulson, R.J., Sauer, M.V., Francis, M.M., Macaso, T.M. and Lobo, R.A. (1994) Factors affecting pregnancy success of human *in vitro* fertilisation in unstimulated cycles. *Human Reproduction* 9, 1571–1575.

Peperrell, R.J. and O'Herlihy, C. (1985) Induction of ovulation with clomiphene, bromocriptine and gonadotrophin-releasing hormone (GnRH). In: *Clinical Reproductive Endocrinology*, Ch. 26, Edinburgh: Churchill Livingstone, pp. 508–522.

RCOG (1992) *Guidlines for Infertility Practice*, London: RCOG.

Rossing, M.A., Daling, J.R., Weiss, N.S., Moore, D.E., and Self, S.G. (1994) Ovarian tumors in a cohort of infertile women. *New England Journal of Medicine* 331, 771–776.

Sandow, J., (1983) Clinical applications of LHRH and its analogues. *Clinical Endocrinology* 18, 571–586.

Silber, S.J., Nagy Zsolt, P., Liu, J., Godoy, H., Devroey, P. and Van Steirteghem, A.C. (1994) Conventional *in vitro* ferilization versus intracytoplasmic sperm injection for patients requiring microsurgical sperm aspiration. *Human Reproduction* **9**, 1705–1709.

Simpson, J.L. (1995) Pregnancy and the timing of intercourse. *New England Journal of Medicine* **333**, 1563–1565.

Skakkeback, N.E., Giwercman, A. and de Kretser, D. (1994) Pathogenesis and management of male inferility. *Lancet* **343**, 1473–1479.

Staessen, C., Hagy, Z.P. Liu, J., Janssenswillen, C., Camus, M., Devroey, P. and Van Stierteghem, A.C. (1995) One year's experience with elective transfer of two good quality embryos in the human *in vitro* fertilisation and intracytoplasmic sperm injection programmes. *Human Reproduction* **10**, 3305–3312.

Strowitzki, T., Kentenich, H., Kiesel, L., Neulen, J. and Bilger, W. (1995) Ovarian stimulation in women undergoing *in vitro* fertilisation and embryo transfer using recombinant human follicle stimulating hormone (Gonal-F) in non-down regulated cycles. *Human Reproduction* **10**, 3097–3101.

Tan, S.L. and Jacobs, H. (1991) *Infertility – Your Questions Answered*, Singapore: McGraw-Hill, p. 16.

Tanbo, T. (1990) Assisted fertilisation in infertile women with patent fallopian tubes. A comparison *in-vitro* fertilisation, gamete infra-fallopian transfer and tubal stage transfer. *Human Reproduction* **5**, 266–270.

Tarin, J.J. (1995) Subzonal insemination, partial zonal dissection or intracytoplasmic injection? An easy decision? *Human Reproduction* **10**, 165–170.

Tournaye, H., Janssens, R., Camus, M., Staessen, C., Devreoy, P. and Van Stertegheim, A. (1993) Pentoxifylline is not useful in enhancing sperm function in cases with previous *in vitro* fertilisation failure. *Fertility and Sterility* **59**, 210–215.

Tsirigotis, M., Craft, I.L., Pelekanos, M., Khalifa, Y., Boulos, A. and Hutchon, S. (1995) In: *Abstracts of the Annual Conference of the BFS*, Liverpool, p. 3.

Tur-Kaspa, I., Maor, Y., Dor, J. and Mashiach, S. (1994) Frequency of intercourse for couples trying to conceive. *Lancet* **344**, 766.

University of Leeds (1992) *Effective Health Care in Action, The Management of Infertility*, August, No. 3.

Wardle, P.G., McLaughin, E.A., McDermott, A., Mitchell, J.D., Ray, B.D. and Hull, M.G.R. (1985) Endometriosis and ovulatory disorder: reduced fertilisation *in vitro* compared with tubal damage and unexplained infertility. *Lancet* **2**, 236–239.

Wilcox, A.J., Weinberg, C.R. and Baird, D.D. (1995) Timing of sexual intercourse in relation to ovulation. *New England Journal of Medicine* **333**, 1517–1521.

Yovich, J.M., Edirisinghe, W.R., Cummins, J.M. and Yovich, J.L. (1990) Influence of pentoxifylline in severe male factor infertility. *Fertility and Sterility* **53**, 715–722.

Chapter 3

The Psychological Experience and Effects of Infertility

Talking to couples who have experienced difficulties conceiving or completing a pregnancy, the same words are used again and again to express their feelings; surprise, denial, anger, guilt, isolation and grief. They were not all experienced by everyone nor all at the same time during the periods of recognition, diagnosis, treatment and outcome. They were, however, common feelings, just as there is a common expectation in much of western society that women will be able to control their fertility, and a common desire to reproduce that has its roots in the conscious and unconscious of the individual and society. A pregnancy belongs to everyone, it ensures the continuity of the individual's genetic heritage and secures the family and the society for the future. The lack of a pregnancy becomes a source of pain for the individual or the couple, and a source of interest and concern for the wider society, which in turn is felt as a pressure by those unable to conceive. The myths of conception are part of the fabric of most societies. There is 'magic' around conception even in the most pragmatic society, where the right atmosphere or place might be sought by the couple, a romantic setting or the safety and comfort of home. In others, the use of

53

dietary changes or 'potions' is part of making a baby. However well educated we are about the mechanics of conception, it is still secret and mysterious enough to encourage the 'magic'. When the mechanics and the magic fail we are left wondering what we did wrong.

History has been hard on women unable to conceive. In the Judaeo-Christian tradition, the Old Testament story of Sarah and Rachel has Rachel seeing her 'barrenness' as a reproach from God. Henry VIII and Napoleon I both abandoned partners because of their inability to bear children. In the present day Princess Diana was reported by the press as having to undergo gynaecological tests before her marriage to Prince Charles. The ability to bear children has been seen to be vital to the social and political life of society.

The psychological barriers to fertility have also been hard on women. Freud's notion of the neurotic woman unable to conceive for unconscious reasons has been very powerful, not just in the way these women have been treated individually, but also in the way this notion has been carried into the wider society with the message that if there is no medically assessed reason for non-conception then there must be an unconscious reason. Writing in 1990, Dinora Pines says that from her clinical experience, many of the infertile women she sees 'have had a difficult, conflicted and frustrating relationship with their own mothers. . . . My clinical experience . . . leads me to believe that they sustain a deep narcissistic wound and regress to a basic body image and state of mind in which they feel unsatisfied by their sexual partners and unsatisfactory to them, as they had once felt to their mothers. Unconsciously they appear to be fixated to an earlier stage in their feminine development in which they feel they have not yet been given permission by their mothers to bear their own babies'. Whilst Dinora Pines may see a very particular group of infertile patients, this feeling of there being some psychological reason behind infertility is one that has been suggested and supported with research many times. It has also crept into the unconscious of society and thus the women affected by infertility. However, this research has been questioned by Edelmann and Connolly (1986) who examined many of the studies to assess the effects of infertility on psychological function and the effects of psychological dysfunction on fertility.

They conclude that 'the issue of psychological causes of infertility remains uncertain'; they do, however, go on to suggest that infertility undoubtedly 'has psychological consequences for some couples'.

These psychological effects are experienced at each stage of the 'process' of infertility, from the time the couple realize that there is a problem with conceiving, throughout the intervention of medicine in diagnosis and treatment, and to the outcome of the treatment whether this results in a pregnancy, the choice to be childless or the option to foster, adopt or find a surrogate parent.

DECIDING TO BE A PARENT

The beginning of the process of childbearing is the recognition of its possibility. Most of us become actively aware that we could produce children at puberty; this is foreshadowed in the games and fantasies of childhood, playing at 'house' or with dolls and soft toys, and imagining ourselves in adult roles. Our identification with our parents or adult care-givers is associated not just with nurturing, but also with sexual activity and the fertility which is taken for granted as part of that sexuality. We will do as they did and produce children as they did.

Control of the production of children is part of our modern education of the child. The knowledge that contraception is generally reliable offers the chance to take total control of fertility. This idea of control is mainly seen as a way of avoiding pregnancy until the choice is made. That choice is affected by many factors: biological, social and financial. The recognition that pregnancy is possible is balanced by the need to feel ready in financial terms, by having achieved certain life goals or by having found a suitable partner. This preparation recognizes the changes that will be brought about by the arrival of a baby and the need to prepare for those changes; thus even at the time of deciding to be pregnant there is already a commitment to change and a subtle reassessment of one's place in society.

For many women it is a commitment to a relationship, heterosexual or lesbian, that provokes the desire to reproduce. A pregnancy is not just the proof, for heterosexuals, of sexual union, but is for everyone a commitment to the relationship, to sharing and hope for the future. The needs of the individual, the couple and their society are to be fulfilled by the pregnancy.

> *Katy was 27 years old when she married Steve. They had known each other for just over a year and had a sexual relationship throughout that time. Katy had had a previous long-term relationship which she had never considered a permanent one. She says that 'I felt quite different about Steve and knew that I wanted his child as soon as possible. I hadn't felt like that before although I had not used contraception very regularly for several years. I somehow didn't mind if I got pregnant but I knew I had PID (pelvic inflammatory disease) and thought I probably wouldn't conceive. Once I was sure that I wanted to be with Steve I went to the doctor to ask about having a baby. I just had not thought before that not getting pregnant even without contraception was a big issue; suddenly it was everything, I wanted Steve's child to show everyone how much we meant to each other and that this was for ever'.*

The mythical child is born when the couple decide not to use contraception and to try to conceive. Many say that at this time their sexual relationship is as good as at the beginning or better. They are relieved of the anxiety of unwanted pregnancy and there is a strong feeling of closeness of purpose and expectation. There are many myths around conception for all societies. This may be around where or when sexual intercourse takes place, superstitious beliefs or purification or dietary restrictions either to increase the likelihood of conception occurring or the chance of having a particular gender child. These all contribute to the 'magic' of conception. When this is not fulfilled, the whole future, the self-esteem and the place in society of the would-be parents is called into question.

NOT CONCEIVING

Infertility is generally defined as the inability to conceive after 1 year of sexual intercourse without contraception. The questionnaires answered in our small survey showed that some people went to their GP after 6 months whilst some waited as long as 5 years. Waiting even 1 year after making the decision seems like a very long time to most couples, particularly if they had never considered not being able to get pregnant. By definition most couples trying to conceive are young and healthy and unless they have had a medical condition that they were aware might cause fertility problems, they have no reason to suspect they will not be in control of their fertility. Many do not expect immediate conception or feel that they may need time for their body to readjust after stopping the pill. Unless they have announced their intention, no-one else is likely to remark on the delay. For many couples the change from sex for fun to sex to procreate adds another dimension to the relationship and it is a time of optimism and joy. It is not surprising then that for many couples it is a slow recognition that they may have a problem with which they will need to seek help.

Pearl was 27 years old and had lived with Paul for 5 years. They had talked about children for a while but Pearl had wanted to finish a teacher training course and work for at least a year. She was a late entry to university and she wanted some proof of her achievement. The decision to start a family was a joint one and they were delighted to stop using contraception which had been a problem for Pearl for several years. They were excited about the thought of a baby and started to make plans for the nursery and discuss when to tell the families. After the first 6 months they talked about seeing the doctor but decided it was a bit early. Pearl's problems with contraception led them to think that it may not be quite straightforward. After 11 months Paul said that he felt they should take the first step. Pearl says that this 'was the first time I cried; all the thoughts I had were focused by Paul, and I thought he must be blaming me and saying I needed to see the doctor. My mother had had some problems conceiving her first child and this had been on my mind; no-one in Paul's family ever seemed to have problems and they all had lots of kids, so I just felt he was blaming me. I refused to see the doctor and we didn't talk about it again for 3 or 4 months. There was hardly a day when I didn't think about it and every period arriving threw me into floods of tears. I had felt so proud of my academic achievement and this was being spoiled as well. I found it hard to concentrate at school and standards began to slip all round. I didn't know who to talk to; several friends already had children and so did my sister; I missed my Mum then more than ever but I'm not even sure that I would have talked to her. I felt there was an assumption that we were having a good time, spending the money and doing what we wanted. I suppose it was my training but the only solution I could see had to be a private one and I set out to find as much information as possible. I said nothing to Paul; we were hardly speaking by then about anything that mattered; I needed to do it for me. It was only when I knew as much as possible that I felt I could go public'.

This disruption of their life plan is often the first feeling of the loss of control that is experienced by so many people who are unable to conceive without help. Having made the adult decision to have a baby they are thrown back into a childlike state by not being able to do what they had assumed all adults were able to do – have a baby without seeking assistance. The loss of control and the need to seek help increases the feeling of vulnerability and leads to the desire to retreat, experiencing fear, anger, guilt and loss.

Several women expressed a need to retreat from their family and friends, sometimes their colleagues and even their partners. They were keenly aware of other people being interested in their fecundity and resented the feeling of pressure this engendered. Women who have chosen to be childless have their conviction to see them through any questions or implied criticism, whereas some infertile women saw any questions as a blow to the heart and a reproach for their failure. Even when the other person did not appear judgemental, their own projection left them feeling inadequate and outside society. They often reported feeling outside the bonds of women with children who were able to make an immediate relationship with each other if only on the basis of this shared experience. Women, strangers to each other, frequently find common ground in stories of pregnancy, child-birth or even the school run. This may be an irritation for the childless from choice, but for the infertile it is another loss. Work colleagues were sometimes distanced for the same reason; men as well as women tried to avoid discussions about families, feeling that the loss of privacy was too great. Those who did tell people often found understanding and sympathy, but a few found that this became too intrusive. The knowledge that the problem has to be shared with professionals meant that some people felt that they needed to preserve their privacy where they could.

Separation from family was often an attempt to avoid the pressure of answering questions about their plans. Some sensed the 'when do you plan to start a family' question as implying that their failure to conceive hid a problem in the relationship, or that they were being selfish and not fulfilling the needs of other people. Protection of the family was mentioned several times as a reason for not telling them what was happening. Some felt that their parents would be upset on their behalf and they were eager to avoid distressing other people.

Many infertile couples reported that as the months and sometimes years went on they started to retreat from their partners, wanting to avoid the bad feelings or hoping that they could keep everything all right if only they did not talk about it. Others were holding onto feelings of fear, anger and guilt. The sexual relationship that had once promised so much for the future was also less of a bond for some couples. It was the focus of their failure and a source of tension and anxiety, disappointment and pain. The couples in 'retreat' could no longer talk about their feelings, and both were making assumptions about how the other felt. Some studies have suggested that the initial disappointment is greater in the women and they take longer to come to terms with the problem (Brand 1989), although once they have decided to embark on treatment, more than half in one study reported that they had experienced some positive effects on the relationship (Cook *et al.* 1989). The early period of discovery and decision-making is more likely to have a negative effect on the relationship.

Both men and women talked about feeling fear: fear for the future and how they would deal with their infertility, fear of the bad feelings and fear of the relationship being permanently adversely affected. The future was hard to contemplate for those who had been certain of their life goals and had never needed to doubt that they would achieve them or who were used to trying hard to get where they wanted. The feeling of not being able to control what was happening to them was frightening to some people who were accustomed to being in control. The strength of bad feelings they experienced frightened some couples; they were unwilling to tell anyone just how angry, guilty, ashamed and isolated they felt. They also felt the need to protect others from these bad feelings which they feared could overwhelm them and their partners and anyone else pulled into the situation. It is also frightening that the difficulty in conceiving could become the reason for the relationship to end. Some felt that they should release their partner to find someone else who could give them a baby, or that they should not have to be a part of the suffering.

Aileen was 34 years old and had been married to Bill for 4 years. She had an 8-year-old daughter from her previous marriage which had ended when her child was 2 years old. Bill had no children and had not been married before. They decided to try to conceive immediately after they were married. After a year Aileen approached the GP. She did not tell Bill and did not express her concern to him. She had conceived the first time without problem and feared that it may be Bill who was infertile. 'I just wanted to protect him. He so wanted his own child and I felt bad that I already had one with no problem. I just hoped that it would be me with the problem. I thought that if it was me I should suggest that he found someone else, I thought I might be too old to be accepted for treatment and felt very hopeless about the whole thing. The only person I told was my cousin who is quite close. She was surprised I was so bothered as I already had Donna and Bill was so fond of her. I felt really alone after that.'

Anger was a very present feeling for many, who were angry in a 'why me' way. They were angry with God or Fate and sometimes felt guilty about this anger. They were also angry in a more direct way, angry with their body letting them down. Many had never had to question their health before and felt cheated that it was such a hidden problem. This anger was sometimes transferred to those around them, the professionals that offered help, friends, family and their partners. This free-floating rage was frightening and sometimes when suppressed became feelings of hopelessness or depression. The most frightening anger was that felt for their partner, blaming them for the lack of a baby and the loss of their hopes for the future. This anger, often recognized as irrational and/or misplaced, can also lead to guilt: guilt that they should be able to deal with the feelings, about blaming their partner, and about outbursts of anger or despair. The guilt may also be related to feelings of shame and remorse: for previous relationships or sexual behaviour, sexually trans-mitted diseases or abortions.

The secrecy, guilt, shame, anger, and the 'retreating' behaviour leads often to feelings of isolation. They may be the only person they know who has experienced difficulty in conceiving. The wish to avoid intrusion, prying and unwanted advice means keeping it secret and secrets leave them isolated, unable to share. The focus on the body, menstrual charts, temperature taking and the most effective way to have intercourse are all private, and the sexual nature of the problem increases the likelihood that it will be difficult or embarrassing to share. It may only be when the woman or couple decides to seek help that the isolation is broken and the secret is out. It may be out in a very public way as several professionals become involved. The vulnerability of the couple or the individual is acute at this time. The attitudes they encounter and the kind of support they receive has an enormous impact on self-esteem, self-image and hopes for the future.

> *Katy and Steve eventually decided that they would see the GP together. Katy found this difficult. 'I had put off talking to Steve about it. When I went to the doctor on my own he said that because of the pelvic inflammatory disease (PID) I might need surgery before I could get pregnant. That made me feel it was a more serious problem than I had thought it was. I knew I had not been pregnant even without using contraception for years but I sort of hoped it was something that could be sorted out easily once I wanted a baby. I couldn't talk to Steve afterwards; I thought it was all my fault about the PID because I had other partners before him and I was totally to blame. The doctor never mentioned that it could be Steve, so I just thought it must be me. I got so down about it that I did begin to talk to Steve, mostly crying and feeling awful. He wanted to know more and insisted that we went to the doctor together. This was the first time he had spoken about it. When we saw the doctor, Steve really wanted information and I wanted to know we would be OK. The doctor arranged a gynae-cology appointment at the local hospital for tests. There was still no one to talk to, it all felt like they were treating an illness and talking about cures and procedures. I needed someone to tell me I was going to have a baby. They just told me I was going to have an operation.'*

SECONDARY INFERTILITY

For those who have already had a child with no assistance, there may have been an expectation that there will be no problem in the future. Finding that they are unable to conceive when they choose will throw all their assumptions about their bodies, their plans for the future and possibly their partner into question. Many of the women we talked to about secondary infertility felt very alone with the problem. Some, who were in new relationships, felt they needed to protect their childless partner. There was sometimes an unspoken thought that it must be the childless one 'to blame' and this was seen as a threat to the relationship. The women who already had a child were often trying to establish a good relationship between the partner and the child, the child and its father and deal with the prospect of not being able to conceive again. Another anxiety that was expressed around this was that it was the partnership that was at fault and a combination of the two of them was the reason for infertility. This was a difficult area to talk about and the element of 'baby magic' was there for some. Other couples who already had children expressed a feeling of pressure from society, family and from within themselves. This was mostly about being selfish.

Lena wrote 'I had one child already and there was a feeling that I was being greedy wanting more. There were women out there who had none and they should have priority, yet I did not feel that we were a proper family. My husband did want another child but it wasn't so important to him and that felt difficult too. I know my family tried to put me off to look after me; they wanted to stop the heartache they thought I would suffer if I tried to get treatment, yet I was suffering just as much because I didn't feel like a proper mother'. Many of these women knew they had a problem but that it was difficult to convince others of how they felt, that they were

63

'*at the bottom of a list and I would be too old by the time I reached the top*'.

WOMEN WITHOUT MALE PARTNERS

Women without male partners and lesbians are in a different situation when they decide to conceive. They do not necessarily have any problem with fertility, and so they are considering the whole issue of assisted conception as soon as they decide they would like to have a child. They will need to trust at least one other person with their plans. One of the difficulties they face is the fear or reality of judgemental attitudes. Some have chosen not to tell anyone that they do not have a male partner and thus maintain a secret throughout. Others find that support from other women in a similar situation gives them the conviction to carry through their plans. Some lesbian women are uncertain about approaching a doctor or clinic for help. They are not sure whether they would be considered for assisted conception as this information is not readily available. They may also be uncertain about staff reactions. Some choose to avoid the health services altogether and inseminate themselves, with the cooperation of a male friend (Saffron 1987).

THE STRESS OF INFERTILITY

Research evidence from infertility clinics shows a raised level of psychosocial distress in patients with prolonged infertility (Wright 1989). However, this work was done with people who have already reached the decision to attempt assisted conception. There is little research among those at an early stage of the awareness of infertility. From interviews and experience it is clear that there is distress, relationship difficulties and anxiety in these early stages that would respond to counselling and support and that patients are asking for this.

Starting Investigations

The first time many couples voiced their fears with another person about not getting pregnant was when they saw their GP. This initial step had great influence on how they were able to proceed with their situation. In our discussions with couples, GPs' reactions were quoted as ranging from 'nothing less than totally supportive' to 'disgustingly insensitive'. It may be that because infertility is not seen as an illness there is confusion in both the client and the professional about how to address the problem. Many couples expressed a desire for 'someone to talk to' even at this stage. Their perception of their problem has much to do with emotional needs as well as requiring the appropriate medical attention to be given.

Being uncertain about what was happening made it more difficult to know what to ask for or expect. Seeking out books and information about infertility can leave the individual once again exposed to judgements by others. For some this search was a way of taking back some control and they used the information they gained to ask their doctor for specific tests to help determine the cause. Sometimes this can feel threatening to the professionals involved and may lead to a feeling of being taken over when really it is a recognition that there is a gap in their provision of service.

GPs may perceive a request for investigations as pre-empting the situation; after all many will conceive spontaneously after 1 year of trying. For those asking, it is their need to know *if* they have a problem that first leads them to their GP. Their concern is that they will be listened to and their anxieties taken seriously. They feel a sense of failure even talking to someone-else; after all, most 'normal' people conceive easily: 'any fool can do it'. The outer world seems concerned with stopping conception and yet their inner world is aching to become a parent 'just like all my family and friends'. A fear of failure even at this stage may prevent individuals from taking part in investigations, and it may also be relevant later when treatment is on offer.

When couples felt their GP took them seriously and instituted a plan of action, they were able to feel a degree of control throughout their investigations, which made them feel more able to cope with their own emotions. It may be the first time that the couple have spoken to each other about their fears, doubts and sadness and yet the feelings of blame and guilt make this area unsafe and many choose to bear their burden silently because they feel too ashamed to speak out.

Donna recognized that though her GP knew what she was going through, she 'didn't think she would have talked about it – not the emotional issues'. Many are then left holding on, with their own coping mechanisms being stretched to their limits. Women are reported to engage coping strategies of avoidance and to seek social support (Stanton and Dunkel-Schetter 1991), whereas men used distancing, self-controlling coping and planned problem solving. In our survey few people felt able to share with others at this stage, but where they did, it was found to be of great benefit. Social support may well assist in adjusting to the stress. Something that came through strongly from our discussions with men was that they felt less able to voice negative emotions because of the supportive role they were expected to play through this stage.

Uncertainty at the beginning of investigations leaves the outcome open-ended and for women the focus on the menstrual cycle is intense. The hopes build up at the beginning of each cycle 'maybe this month – 2 days late – we've cracked it – then oh no it isn't *again!*'. This demonstrates an emotional roller-coaster effect of raising hopes only to have them dashed.

Their defences at this point are sometimes unable to protect them from the fear of helplessness. So much seems to be invested in determining when ovulation occurs and timing sexual intercourse (the hopeful phase) and then daily searching for signs of a pregnancy or a period (the watchful phase) to the realization that the hope is gone (the painful phase) and yet there must be hope to carry on for the next cycle. It is the hope that is able to push away the pain and keep the goal of parenthood alive.

Men appear to be less engaged with the emotional aspects at this point, feeling that they need to remain strong and support their partner. In so doing they choose to repress uncomfortable feelings that threaten self-esteem and adopt a positive attitude towards the outcome of investigations. They may use the investigations which are more focused on the woman to allow them to maintain their distance without having to address their own feelings of guilt and shame. We found that men did experience many of the feelings voiced by their partners but they were less likely to express them at this stage. It was often not possible to hear their issues until they had progressed to treatment, where the counselling alliance gave them the space to voice their concerns. This perceived gender difference may not hold true in all cultures but certainly appears in western cultures.

Questions about intimate sexual practices can reveal innermost feelings about the self laid down in childhood. This can be seen as very exposing and the individual feels quite vulnerable. There also may be issues about past behaviour affecting their situation now leading to feelings of guilt and shame.

The invasion of privacy around sexual function can be experienced as a threat to potency. Masculinity and the ability to father a child are inextricably linked in the psyche even though the man's instinctual drives are thought to be more focused on a need for pleasure and gratification. The realization that he may never father a child is deeply wounding to his psyche.

In many cultures men do not display emotions as easily as women. Their traditional role is to comfort and protect. Women often say that they don't know how their partner is feeling about their problem because 'he doesn't seem to need to talk about it'. This in turn can lead to 'he doesn't seem to care about it'. This is often not the case. Men do hold back when they see and hear the distress of their partner but this does not mean that they do not feel sadness and loss. It usually means that they do not know how to express or manage these feelings and so repress them, reasoning that they need to stay strong and in control to support their partner. Couple disharmony may be the result of this lack of communication.

Many men feel that the concentration on investigating the woman left them outside the problem and they are seen as 'sperm providers' without recognition and status. Even when there were sperm problems men reported huge differences in the way they were told.

John's partner received a phone call from their doctor after one sperm test. He said, 'Well we've found out why you aren't getting pregnant; John is infertile. Make an appointment to come and see me if you want. I think you will have to consider adoption now'. They were devastated with this news and did not return to see their doctor until they had a second opinion at a private fertility clinic.

Women also experience a loss of femininity, a sense of feeling incomplete and empty. Sex takes on a different meaning and the initial excitement experienced at stopping contraception changes to a constant reminder of failure.

Allowing someone else into the problem was experienced by some as a relief. It took away some of the anxiety as another takes on some of the responsibility. There was comfort to be gained from taking action and each can be seen to be contributing to changing the situation. When couples felt there was a plan to their investigations they were able to focus on the task of completing samples, blood tests, scans and planning appointments. For some there was much work to be done around who and what to tell at work about the time off they would need. All of this helped them to have a positive attitude. They felt they were solving the problem in finding out why.

Diagnosis

When diagnosis offers a reason why conception has not taken place then the fantasy that all may be all right is lost. The belief was that diagnosis would in itself solve the problem, which has become why can't we have a child? There was also magical thinking that it could be solved easily and this no longer appears to be the case. The loss of assumed fertility is now a reality and becomes a conscious problem. The longed-for mythical child feels further away now and even though there are treatments, they only alleviate the problem; there are no cures and no certainty of ever becoming a parent. Taking on the identity of infertility now means accepting it for life. This identity changes not only the way the self is perceived but also the way others will perceive the self thus change is inevitable. Even if there is a child then fertility is relieved but cannot be cured. Only in circumstances not fully explainable in the medical literature will someone conceive spontaneously from now on. If there is a problem that can be identified as belonging to one or other of the couple then both re-examine their feelings towards themselves and towards their partner.

Women traditionally have accepted the responsibility for infertility within many cultures and have suffered loss of status in patriarchal societies. Finding a medical cause within the woman may lead to medical treatment to repair the problem, for example, tubal surgery or correction of anovulation which on its own can result in a pregnancy. For some though, treatment will mean choosing to move on to more technical assisted conception techniques. Some talk of a sense of relief that their partner's sperm was normal and the cause of infertility lay with them. When there were problems with sperm, some women chose to imply to family and friends that they were the one with the problem, believing that they could cope with the reactions and needing to protect their partner.

Many men were devastated to find that they may never become genetic parents and they were often surprised at their reaction. This may arise out of their unwillingness to admit to themselves the depth of their desire to be a father.

John hadn't thought much about what becoming a father meant to him until he was told about his poor sperm. He said, 'Many feelings came flooding in and I couldn't quite handle them all at once. I didn't know who to talk to about this. I was feeling much too guilty to talk with my partner. I just couldn't talk with my family. I felt too ashamed. As for my friends – well it's not the thing you talk about over a pint of beer'. Soon after hearing the information he was challenged about what to do about it. He said, 'Shirley started talking about using donor sperm or adoption and I just freaked out. I mean I wasn't anywhere near thinking about that. How could she dismiss me, didn't she care how I was feeling,

69

> *and yet I knew that if we were to have any*
> *chance of becoming parents I would have to*
> *consider those possibilities'.*

The belief that diagnosis will solve *the problem*, (which has become, 'Why can't we have a child?) is shattered when no cause can be found and no diagnosis made. There is still no prospect of a child and now the most common reaction is 'there must be a reason'. Couples who cannot be given a clear medical reason for their infertility (commonly referred to as unexplained infertility) are left with a sense of failure again, and at a loss to know how to deal with the blame and guilt. Often they will spend much time examining in minute detail anything that could have contributed to their problem. Social patterns are put up for questioning. Is it my partner's genetic background – her aunt had four miscarriages? There's nothing like that in our family. What happened before we became a couple? What about previous other partners? Is it because I smoke? Should he stop drinking? There is little evidence to suggest that changing factors such as diet or smoking will definitely result in conception but for some there is comfort to be felt at owning a problem and doing something about it. It may also enable them to feel in control.

Each is left feeling a deep sense of guilt and blame, with a falling self-esteem and hopelessness growing out of their anger. In the absence of identification of a physical reason each assumes a psychological reason and blames each other.

At this time there is the risk of disturbance of the couple's relationship, as there is too much dangerous ground between them to share any more. Emotional investment in the relationship at this stage may be too much and there are reports of relationship breakdown. Long-term relationship problems that would have threatened the relationship at some time may come to the surface at this time. These may not be a direct result of the stress of infertility but are related to it. Certainly, the relationship undergoes change and many said the experience had brought them closer together.

Both men and women often said that it was at this time that they wanted to talk to someone, as there was much to talk about. Important decisions need to be made, such as what happens next and where do we go from here? This was a time of uncertainty and confusion for many, and it raised issues about loss of control. Both women and men said that whilst doctors were quick to offer and outline possible courses of action, they felt stunned and unable to hear what was being said. 'How can you hear options for treatment when your world has fallen apart?'.

> *Jan and Ian were both married for the second time. Neither had any children from their first marriages and took time before they decided to try and start a family. Jan was diagnosed as having endometriosis. She says, 'my condition was ignored and IVF recommended. I had to read Issue's booklets and pamphlets and inform myself . There was no IVF centre near me so I was referred to ******. There was no under-standing that we had family and work commit-ments and treatment had to be flexible, or that individuals and couples respond in different ways and to different things. Ian became clinically depressed and needed special counsel-ling, first on his own. I was upset at having endometriosis and everyone seemed to ignore that. The result was that for months we couldn't talk to each other'.*

Treatment: Making the Decision

Progressing to treatment happened quickly for some but for others there were many factors to be taken into consideration. Finances had an important part to play in this, as many licensed clinics are within the private sector. Referral to NHS clinics depended for many on their geographical location and there were long waits. Feelings of despair leading to depression were common at this time. The value placed by society on parenting seems at odds with its provision of service. As the individual looks at the options available, the stress of decision-making hinges on the need to 'pursue every possibility, however remote and costly, in an effort to overcome the inability to have children' (Snowden and Snowden 1994). The prospect of taking part in the new medical and scientific advances that are now on offer can be overwhelming for some and with heartache they decide to stop before their coping mechanisms are pushed too far. They hide their pain and little has been researched or written about how they come to terms with their decisions and at what personal cost.

The national support groups appeared to offer much to couples at this point. They felt they could hear about others with similar problems without having to identify themselves and for some this was a lifeline. Others were able to channel their anger by joining the groups that demand a better deal for the infertile.

As well as coping with their own feelings, those in a couple relationship are required to focus on the other partner. The negotiations required to rebuild the relationship without the prospect of children can be overwhelming. Those who progressed on to treatment were able to bury their anxieties about this as they concentrated their energies on believing it could still happen.

Deciding where to go was sometimes left to the couples themselves. To some, this felt as if they were left alone to do all the work themselves and others felt that it gave them a degree of control over their future.

Undergoing Treatments

Concentrating on the physical aspects of treatment offers space for the mind to stop worrying for a time. They can let go of the fear that nothing is going to happen and be involved in their physical state. They hand over control to the professionals.

Many couples dealt with their loss of control by investing their carers with complete control, 'We just put ourselves in their hands'. The individual ceases to have any part in the process so if it doesn't work then he/she cannot be to blame. The fantasy that the team of doctors, nurses and embryologists make all things possible allows the anger felt within when it doesn't work to be projected onto the team or any one member of the team. It feels unsafe to own this anger but, unfortunately, the team is still needed if another treatment cycle is considered and so the anger must be denied or repressed. Loss of control can also be experienced when those outside the self appear to know more about the mechanics of the body in relation to its ability to reproduce. This is reflected again if treatment is successful and a pregnancy occurs. They may again experience anxiety about the ability of the body to function normally if it hasn't in the past.

Starting out on treatments such as Clomid, PIO, IUI, IVF, DI or surrogacy, many couples felt a sense of new beginnings and feelings of hope and excitement were rekindled. There was much activity to be engaged with, in planning treatment and organizing other aspects of life such as work and social arrangements.

Many refer to the 'roller coaster' effect on the emotions. A state of anticipation and hope leads to feelings of anger, despair and depression. In coping with these feelings, individuals reacted in many different ways. For some, confronting the problem enabled them to feel in charge and set limits for this particular goal. This worked well when both partners were in agreement but caused distress when there were differences.

Individuals had their own perception of how their partner was dealing with their situation. Many women expressed a feeling that 'it doesn't seem to matter so much to him', reflecting fears about his commitment, his need to be a father or her need for him to acknowledge her needs and fears. Men sometimes agreed that they did not realize the depth of the need experienced by their partner and they were hesitant to express themselves, fearing that their partner could not cope with this load. This has echoes in the processes involved in early pregnancy when men perceive their role as protector.

For those embarking on treatments involving donor gametes, eggs, sperm or embryos, there is a loss of genetic parenting. This loss demands recognition and if possible needs to be attended to before referral is accomplished so that there is an opportunity to look at the psychological implications of the proposed medical treatment. A sense of guilt of the infertile partner can lead some to accepting treatment quickly without paying attention to the loss and bereavement experienced by the self or the partner. Many clinics ask those using donor gametes to attend a counselling session before they embark on treatment. This offers space for the couple to bring in their own issues concerning the proposed treatment. Contact with the support group specifically concerned with Donor Insemination -DI Networks, gives those contemplating the use of donor sperm another opportunity to discuss their anxieties and identify a source of peer group support. A new dimension now enters their lives, that of the fantasy donor, and the implications of having a child not genetically related to either one or the other or both are difficult areas to explore without the expert help of the counsellor.

Couples whose only treatment option is surrogacy, which is dependent on IVF, most commonly arrive at a clinic with a surrogate. They will already have a relationship with their surrogate, who may be a family member, a friend or someone they have met through an agency. They will have been looking at the positive aspects of surrogacy, sometimes not wanting to pay much attention to the implications and potentially negative consequences. The surrogate mother may be alone or in a relationship and, in law, can only offer her services voluntarily. Pursuing this form of treatment means summoning the emotional energy required to carry them all through their efforts towards achieving parenthood. Looking at all the implications surrogacy raises may be difficult because of a need to continue in the belief that it could work. Historically, surrogacy arrangements are perceived as having the potential to undermine the accepted meaning of mother and father and the Bible reports consequences not envisaged at the start of the proceedings. For instance, Hagar, the first surrogate mother, despises Sarah the woman who commissioned her, and in turn has to flee into the wilderness to get away from the harsh treatment metered out by Sarah after the birth (Genesis, Ch.16). These effects can destroy relationships and may affect the welfare of the child born by such arrangements. Many surrogacy agreements that do not require IVF are entered into and are successful. Studies have not yet been undertaken to review the outcome in terms of psychological effects on any of the participants. Links have been made with research indicating that women who place their children for adoption suffer long-term loss and guilt: 'It can be argued that surrogate mothers may well experience similar serious negative and long term consequences' (Blyth 1995).

Ending Treatment

Deciding to stop treatment can be a positive decision made by the individual or the couple who feel they can no longer invest their hopes and dreams solely in this area. There may be a medical reason to stop; indeed, some hope that the team will tell them to stop so that they can avoid looking at this aspect themselves. The responsibility of making that decision is felt to be too heavy a burden by others and they carry on having treatment after treatment with no real hope of success.

> *After six attempts at IVF, Valerie said, 'It's too painful to get off the bandwagon so we just keep going on. I live in fear that someone will say no and I will have to face up to what to do with myself. Coming here, I met others like me for the first time and I didn't feel alone any more. Leaving here means looking at the fact that I will never be a mother – I just can't think of how my life would be without children'.*

To end there needs to be space to acknowledge and work through the loss of the dreamed-about family. Then there can be a focusing on options for re-evaluating life goals.

Becoming Pregnant

Women who became pregnant expressed needs during the first few months that were to do with feeling valued and cared for. After finding out there was a viable pregnancy they often said goodbye to those they had shared much intimacy with and were anxious about who would now be there for them. Many returned to the clinic with queries and questions and wanted further acknowledgement that they were still pregnant. This may have something to do with taking back responsibility for their own bodies. They may have ceased to expect their body to be able to function in a normal way and be unable to process any information given to them in the belief that it can't apply to them because of their special circumstances.

*Leonie's first attempt at IVF had been abandoned
because only one small follicle grew in response
to the stimulation. Her next attempt was viewed
with much anxiety and happily resulted in a
pregnancy. There were many phone calls and
questions about aches and pains and nausea.
She said, 'I was so worried that something would
go wrong. I had to keep asking and checking
things out. I didn't know whether it was OK not
to eat if I felt so sick, after all what will happen to
the baby? I can't let it suffer'.*

The concern is also around the preciousness of the pregnancy. Much has been invested in getting pregnant: will others take notice of that and act accordingly? This feeling may continue into the child's life and although research indicates that children born through the assisted conception techniques have the same social and emotional make-up as their naturally conceived peers (Golombok *et al.* 1995), the degree of stress involved in coping with parenting for those who have waited years for their children has not been elucidated.

REFERENCES

Blyth, E. (1995) *Infertility and Assisted Conception. Practice Issues for Counsellors*, Birmingham: BASW.

Brand, H. (1989) The influence of sex differences on the acceptance of infertility. *Journal of Reproductive and Infant Psychology* 7, 129–132.

Cook, R., Parsons, J., Mason, R. and Golombok, S. (1989) Emotional, marital and sexual functioning in patients embarking on IVF and AID treatment for infertility. *Journal of Reproductive and Infant Psychology* 7, 87–94.

Edelmann, R. and Connolly, K. (1986) Psychological aspects of infertility. *British Journal of Medical Psychology* 59, 209–219.

Golombok, S., Cook, R., Bish, A. and Murray, C. (1995) *Families Created by the New Reproductive Technologies: Quality of Parenting and Social and Emotional Development of the Children*, Research project, City University, (1990) London.

Pines, D. (1990) Emotional aspects of infertility and its remedies. *International Journal of Psychoanalysis* 71, 561.

Saffron, L. (1987) *Getting Pregnant Our Own Way: a Guide to Alternative Insemination*, London: Women's Health Information Centre.

Snowden, R. and Snowden, E. (1994) *The Gift of a Child*, Exeter: University of Exeter Press.

Stanton, A. L. and Dunkel-Schetter C. (Eds) (1991) *Infertility Perspectives from Stress and Coping Research*, New York: Plenum Press.

Wright, J. (1989) Psychosocial distress and infertility: a review of controlled research. *International Journal of Fertility* **34**, 126–142.

Chapter 4

Counselling Theories and Skills

Whilst there are many 'schools' of counselling and therapy that may offer appropriate help for women and men seeking advice, information and support with the problem of infertility, the principles underlying the practice of counselling and the skills and personal attributes of the therapist are common.

They are directed to helping the client to identify and explore feelings about their situation and ways in which it may be resolved or improved. The individual counsellor working in the field of infertility will need to decide for themselves which type of therapy seems most in keeping with their own philosophy and views of counselling practice and seek training in this area. However, it may be useful to have a brief knowledge of other therapies that clients may have used or may be referred to for help.

PSYCHODYNAMIC OR PSYCHOANALYTIC THERAPY

Psychoanalytic theory developed from the work of Sigmund Freud, a doctor who was working in Vienna at the beginning of this century. It is the basis from which all psychotherapy started and other well known therapists such as Jung, Adler and Klein developed their work from that of Freud.

It is concerned with unconscious motives and drives. The unconscious mind develops from our earliest experiences and affects our conscious mind at all times. It accounts for our behaviour, thoughts and feelings. Experiences in the past that were not dealt with at the time will be echoed by similar experiences in the present; this may lead to anxiety and depression, as well as neurotic behaviour.

The model is based on the personal involving three elements: the id, ego and super-ego. The id has our basic drives for food, comfort and pleasure. The ego has been developed and refined by contact with the world and works on the 'reality principle'. The super-ego develops as we grow up and absorbs our parental and cultural influences. It is our 'morality principle' and is there to contain the id. It is the seat of conscience and judgement. Freud believed that these elements need to be in harmony for good psychological health and yet all the time there is conflict and compromise. The anxiety produced by the conflict leads us to develop defence mechanisms to cope with it, and also to contain the powerful forces of the id. These ego defence mechanisms include:

- *Sublimation* – the redirection of instinctive drives into acceptable activity such as aggression directed into sports.
- *Repression* – pushing unacceptable feelings back into the unconscious. If this is incomplete it can lead to insecurity, guilt and low self-worth, or the neurotic expression of feelings.
- *Regression* – returning to childlike behaviour when we do not want to accept responsibility.
- *Denial* – the avoidance of bad reality, wishes or feelings. This may result in the true meaning of the feelings being distorted.
- *Projection* – ascribing unacceptable desires or feelings to others. This may lead to blaming others or projecting anger or hostility onto them rather than owning it.

Other defence mechanisms are displacement, reaction formation, compensation and introjection.

Freud and other psychoanalysts used interpretation, free association and dream analysis to help uncover the unconscious and bring it into consciousness, thus reducing the conflict and anxiety, and the use of unhelpful defence mechanisms. The therapy requires the client to recall and explore past experiences, however painful and distressing this may be.

In practice, the approach is helpful for people wanting to explore the relationship between the past and the present, to help them understand the unconscious motivation behind what may seem to be inexplicable or repeatedly damaging behaviour. It may also help the client to deal with painful experiences in their past which continue to cause anxiety or distress. However, it is a long-term therapy requiring a strong commitment from both client and therapist and therefore rarely available on the NHS.

Training for psychoanalysis is long, requiring study and supervised work, at an intensive level.

CLIENT-CENTRED THERAPY

Developed in the second half of this century in the USA, this theory challenged the rather determinist ideas of psychoanalysis. Carl Rogers (1991 edition), one of the best known exponents, developed what he called the 'client centred approach'. Rogers believed that clients could find their own way through problems and were essentially responsible for themselves. Rogers called this the 'actualizing tendency'. This is the theory that each individual has the capacity to grow and develop, to reach a maximum potential in life. The therapist is there to guide the process and reflect back to the client their own words and issues. This reflective technique encourages the client to 'hear' what they are saying and take responsibility for it. Rogers believed that people are essentially 'good' and will be able to find the solution with the counsellor acting as a guide rather than the expert with all the answers.

Rogers developed a model of effective relationships with the client using three key features: congruence, unconditional positive regard and empathy. These will be examined in more depth later in this book.

Abraham Maslow (1968) also contributed to the client centred theoretical approach. He is probably best known for his 'hierarchy of needs', which he believed to be responsible for human motivation. These begin with the Basic Physical Needs (water, food and oxygen) and move through Safety Needs,

81

Relationship Needs, Esteem Needs to Self-Actualization Needs. This last is the drive towards self-fulfilment and knowledge. Like Rogers, Maslow had an optimistic view of peoples' drive towards 'healthy tendencies'.

The therapy may be helpful when clients feel they are controlled by circumstances and need to reassert their own control over their lives. Therapists have a thorough training and are supervised in their practice. It is possible to consider shorter term therapy with this technique and it is one that many counsellors use.

RATIONAL-EMOTIVE THERAPY

This is concerned with the idea that how we think affects how we feel. If we change our way of thinking about ourselves, our incorrect beliefs, we will be able to improve our self-image and confidence in our ability to cope with our lives.

Albert Ellis (1990) began developing this theory in the USA in the 1950s. He combined his interests in psychoanalysis, behavioural psychology and philosophy in his work on rational-emotive therapy. He believed that people have a capacity for irrational as well as rational thinking and that the irrational thinking is at the root of unhappiness. He states in his 'ABC model' of emotional disturbance that it is not what happens at A that causes the unhappiness but the 'self-talk' of the individual at B, which is felt as disturbance at point C.

Ellis believed that people continue with assumptions about relationships and life acquired in childhood . These may become unhelpful in adult life. Ellis stated that there are 12 typical irrational beliefs that people hold about themselves and which prevent them living how they might want to. These include 'It is necessary that I be loved or approved of by everyone for everything I do', 'I need someone or something stronger or greater than myself upon which I can rely' and 'I must be good at everything I do at all times. Otherwise I am not a worthwhile person'. The therapist confronts and challenges those beliefs that may be preventing the client from living their life effectively. The counsellor tries to understand the client and communicate this understanding and acceptance. There is not the emphasis on empathy as in the client-centred approach but a need for the therapist to remain outside the client's irrational thought patterns. This is a rational approach to problem solving that may help to encourage the client to develop a more realistic outlook on life and encourage clear thinking at a time when clients are overwhelmed by emotions.

GESTALT THERAPY

The German word 'gestalt', which has no real equivalent in English, means something like 'whole' and 'structure'. The therapy was developed by Fritz and Laura Perls (1969) drawing on psychoanalysis and philosophy. The theory emphasizes the relationship between psychological and physical states. It is particularly concerned with what is happening 'here and now' for the client. It does not explore past experiences, but encourages the client to be aware of how they are thinking, feeling and sensing in the present, as well as what they are avoiding. This involves a total participation of the client: intellectual, spiritual, emotional and physical. It is aiming for 'wholeness' so all parts of the client are attended to. Gestalt therapy is concerned with how people become aware of their needs in relation to their total environment. This helps the client to make sense of what is happening and places the client in charge; the therapist is not making interpretations. The counsellor is creative rather than interpretative, using role-play and techniques such as 'the empty chair' to encourage self-awareness. The therapist may direct the client's attention to certain behaviours or body language to help the process of awareness. Each counselling session is unique, and does not rely on a continuous exploration of the client's history. It may be confrontational or challenging within the trusting relationship of the counselling alliance.

Gestalt therapy may be helpful to clients who are avoiding dealing with their present state of mind or those who 'bottle up' their feelings. It helps people to become more aware and this awareness leads to taking responsibility for their lives.

TRANSACTIONAL ANALYSIS

Developed by Eric Berne (1964) in the USA, transactional analysis (TA) is a way of helping people to look at their relationships. It aims to use clearly understood language with no mystique. It is based on the concept of three 'ego states', Parent, Adult and Child. These are common to us all and direct our thoughts and feelings. We develop the Parent state from our own experience of being parented, with the direct instructions and the 'shoulds' that we have been given. It includes the skills for living that we have been taught. However, these are not always appropriate for the adult and may be a reason for poor communication. When we operate in the Parent state we may be judgemental and patronizing, we talk down to people. Our childhood experiences become the Child Ego state, in which we may become dependent and submissive or perhaps the naughty or rebellious child. It includes our Free Child and what Berne called our 'Adapted Child', the one who has learned to please. It is in the Adult state that we relate to others in a mature way and as equals. It is our logical and realistic response to our environment. It can be helpful for clients (and therapists) to examine how they function within a relationship. This 'mapping' of the ego state relationships can show how a relationship may be unbalanced and the partners play 'games' to maintain their positions.

Transactional analysis can be used by couples seeking to examine their relationships and help them to become more assertive about their feelings and also identify more adult ways of solving conflicts. The therapist is encouraged to establish clear communication with clients and to de-mystify the process.

Another major therapy is behaviour therapy, or behaviour modification, which is a scientific examination of how behaviours are established and reinforced. Change comes from learning new behaviours and practising them.

This is by no means a complete list of therapies available (see appendix). One element they have in common is the need for thorough training and supervision in the particular therapy.

MODELS OF COUNSELLING

Models of therapy differ from theories in that they offer a way of working rather than a framework of belief about development and relationships. It may be useful for those counselling people with problems of fertility to consider some models of counselling which can be used to help them examine their feelings and explore how they want to move forward in their lives. Using a model helps to bring structure to the counselling process. To make it more than 'having a chat' when the client expects to have some support or help to change.

Egan's Three-Stage Model of Counselling

Egan (1986) developed a three-stage model of counselling that could be used in a non-directive way to help the client 'manage' their world. These three stages are:

(1) identifying and clarifying the problem
(2) development of goals
(3) action.

The stages are also divided into present scenario, future scenario and how to achieve change. In the first stage the counsellor helps the client to explore the present situation. It is important to tell the story, partly because the story may never have been told before and also because only from the whole story may the problems emerge. Often clients will say 'I don't know what is happening to me'; they are aware of feeling stressed or distressed but may find it too frightening to look at the whole picture. It feels too overwhelming without help. For the infertile client this may mean looking at the problem beyond 'I want to have a baby and I can't' to all the other pressures that exist for them around their inability to conceive. The next stage, goal setting, involves choosing preferred scenarios within a realistic framework. The preferred goal may be to have a baby but they may be helped to look at the other life goals they have. The final stage is action. This allows the client to identify areas where they can take some control. All methods of achieving their goals can be explored and the client is encouraged to think of how they may implement them.

Throughout the process there is a need for constant evaluation. The client and the counsellor must be reflecting on their progress through the stages. This helps the process to move on and not become 'stuck' at one stage.

Truax and Carkuff's Model

Truax and Carkuff also designed a helping model (Carkuff 1987) setting out their three goals as exploration, understanding and action. This is a circular model in that action itself produces feedback, which generates further exploration and thus more accurate self-awareness. Alongside the model they identify the skills needed as attending, responding, personalizing the experience and initiating action.

COUNSELLING SKILLS

There are skills common to all models of therapy, most of which are about 'being' with the client. Unlike nursing or teaching where the helper is able to 'do' something to improve the situation, in counselling the therapist has often just to be alongside the client, to hear their story, to 'hold' their pain and distress, their anger and sadness, until they are ready to move on and take some control for themselves. Then the counsellor has to empower them to go on and be able to let go. There are also skills that are involved with developing a safe place for the client, giving time and space, questioning and reflecting and dealing with the client's anger, silence or confrontational behaviour.

The central skills, are listening and attending. Without these the client will not be able to feel safe or 'held', or to feel that their experience is validated.

Listening

This skill is central to the counselling process; it is concerned with hearing the other person, not just the things that they say but the words that they use, the paralinguistic elements of their speech and their non-verbal communication.

The language that the client uses, its words, metaphors and phrases, conveys how he or she is feeling. The paralinguistic aspects of speech may also help to convey the whole picture. This includes the pitch and tone of voice, the 'ums' and silences and the fluency of speech. We must be careful not to make assumptions from this but we can check our observations with the client. If they sound depressed or hesitant we may be able to express our perception to them. Similarly, with non-verbal communication, the use of gesture, facial expression and touch may be reflected back to the client. However, we must remember that these vary with cultural background. They are a guide to be checked with the client, not an absolute. Listening requires the hearer to be quiet. This may sound simple but many of us find it very difficult to remain silent and attentive for long. This is particularly true when the counsellor feels under pressure of time or space. Think how rarely you are totally silent; try listening to the sounds around you, the sounds of your own body. Try to remember the words of even a short conversation and you will realize how infrequently we just listen. We may also be prevented from quietness by our own internal pressure to say the right thing or make interpretations; we cannot listen if we are working out the next question in our heads. Listening takes practice and needs constant monitoring. It also benefits from practice with another person.

Attending

Attending is the other major skill of counselling. It is the act of focusing on the other person with a conscious awareness of what they are communicating to us. We can often recognize this best if we reflect on times when we were not attended to, e.g. simple things such as waiting in a shop when the assistant finishes a conversation or on the telephone when we are asked to repeat something. These are minor things; when a client is telling of pain or confusion, not to be attended to is distressing and feels as if the issue is being trivialized. There may have been times when someone has said to us 'you weren't listening': you can repeat their words but they knew that the attention was not there.

To be of help to our clients we need to be focused on them. We cannot be effective if distracted by our own thoughts or feelings, by sounds outside in the corridor or a phone call we are expecting. The client needs you to be there alongside them. Just as we may read our client's body language so may they read ours: our level of attention is there to see. When we are working with clients from a different culture to our own we may have to work more intensively to be alongside our client, trying to understand their world. We must also respect their feelings about this attention. For some this may be seen as intrusive or may only be a part of work done with the whole family.

Attending includes giving time and space. The client who feels hurried may feel very unimportant. The exploration of feelings and thoughts is a crucial part of the counselling process and this cannot be hurried. It does not mean that you have to give unlimited time to every client but you do need to make the boundaries clear. If the client understands that the session is for half an hour, it allows them to work within it. The same is true of space. Respect for the needs of clients means that we need to find somewhere where they feel safe to be upset or angry or to talk confidentially. If they are concerned that someone can overhear or may come into the room they will not feel free to talk.

Exploring

We explore in order to discover. Exploration is the start of counselling but it is also a continuing process. We start as we said before with the story and in exploring the story begin to find the feelings and thoughts that go along with it. To encourage this exploration the counsellor needs to give permission for the client to express themselves, without judgement or sympathy. If the counsellor can offer empathy, by being alongside and entering the world of the client, it may enable the client to feel safe to explore. There may need to be more active participation from the helper, asking open-ended questions or brainstorming possible changes or choices. Clarifying and summarizing may also be part of the exploration, allowing the client to assess their progress and direction.

Questioning

Clients can feel attacked and vulnerable if questions are asked without them understanding the reason or in a way that feels judgemental. Yet we may have to ask questions as part of counselling, especially if we need to take a history. Explaining the reason for the questions can make some people feel more comfortable with it. The most effective way is to ask open-ended questions, giving the client the chance to explain rather than just to answer directly. To ask 'I wonder why you felt that?' may elicit a more helpful answer for the client than 'why did you do that?'. 'How do you feel about not being able to give your partner a child?' will allow more exploration and feel less judgemental than 'do you feel bad about not giving your partner a child?'. It is important that our questions do not suggest the answer. This is particularly important at times when the client may feel that they have to please the helper. 'Surely you don't think that?' is a very difficult thing to answer if you feel that you need to get it right. We may need to ask probing questions, but again they can be phrased to help the client explore the answer. 'How did you feel after that?' or 'perhaps you could tell me how that felt for you', allows them to take the story further.

Reflecting

This skill is very much part of the client-centred approach. It is giving back to the client the words that they have said, so that they may hear them clearly. At a more advanced level it is also feeding back to the client not just the words but the implications of those words.

Client: I find it upsetting when my sister comes over with her baby.

Counsellor: You find it hard to be with your sister and her baby.

Client: Yes, she wants me to hold the baby and play with her and talks about baby things all the time.

Counsellor: You feel your sister wants you to be involved with her baby.

Client: I just can't do it, it makes me angry. I want her support with what I'm going through. Then I feel bad that I don't want to see her baby.

Counsellor: You don't feel your sister understands how you feel.
Client: No one does.

The reflective technique has been used here to move on from actual words to what the counsellor felt may be behind the words. This gave the client permission to express her feelings.

SOME DIFFICULT COUNSELLING ISSUES

Some areas of counselling are always challenging to the therapist as well as the client. These include silence, anger, confrontation and endings.

Silence

Silence is particularly difficult if the counsellor is unsure or does not understand why the silence is there. It can be helpful to the client and it is important not to see it as a negative. The client may be thinking or reflecting; it may be one of the few times when they are permitted silence without explanation or justification. It is important for the counsellor to feel able to allow the space, and not to fill it themselves. If the silence continues or the client seems disturbed by it then reflecting back the client's last words may be a gentle way to break it. People who are depressed may be silent for long periods and the counsellor may need to be aware of the client's general state of mind. There may also be angry silences, when the client is unwilling or unable to say what they feel, fearing the destructiveness of their anger.

Anger

Clients who are stressed or anxious may respond with anger or irritability. They sometimes express feelings about being let down by the professionals who have failed to solve their problem. This is sometimes in response to what they understood to be promises of a solution. It is important to acknowledge anger and allow its expression if this is safe. We also have to remember that some anger is a defence mechanism, perhaps a projection of the bad feelings the client is carrying. Helping the client to explore where the anger belongs may help to make it feel less frightening and burdensome.

Confrontation

The expectation of confrontation may build up so much anxiety in the counsellor that he or she may seek to avoid it, or become so unclear that the client does not understand the issue or, from a wish to 'get it over with', jump in with both feet. To avoid it feeling like a direct attack it may be helpful to warn the client. Beginning with 'I think there is a difficulty we need to discuss' makes it clear that this is a shared area not a direct attack. The client needs time to understand the issues and space to work out their feelings. The counsellor may also be able to suggest a way forward in discussion, always giving the client an opportunity to move out if they want to.

Endings

It can be difficult for both the client and the counsellor to end sessions. Even a single session may be hard to finish, so often a client will make their most important remark as they get up to go!

Ending the session well may start at the beginning. The client needs to have a clear idea of the time they have so that they can choose how much they feel able to deal with. If the issue of confidentiality is also made clear at the beginning it may help the client not to carry anxiety at the end about how much they have revealed. It is very common for people to feel awkward or embarrassed about what they have revealed, and it may be helpful for the therapist to reassure them of this. Some clients also feel concerned about 'burdening' the counsellor. This may indicate their own feelings of being burdened or their uncertainty about whether the counsellor can 'hold' the story and the feelings aroused. Ending contact altogether can seem like

91

a bereavement when there has been a good and helping relationship with the therapist. For some clients for whom loss is a real difficulty, there may need to be considerable preparation for the ending. The counsellor may use this as an opportunity to help the client to look at past experiences of loss and to identify positive coping strategies. For some people it is the time for a push towards independence and encouragement that they can cope alone. If the counsellor has worked empathically with a client then he or she will have 'been alongside', perhaps through a very painful time, and may also have feelings about ending. There is pleasure in seeing a client move towards health and independence, but for some counsellors letting go may be difficult. One should look to counter-transference, the feelings that the therapist develops for the client (see Chapter 5), to explain the feelings. Most helpers worry that they are doing the helping for the wrong motives at some time. It is not wrong to want to be needed, but it is wrong to transfer this to a personal demand on the client. If the therapist concentrates on the work and the process of counselling, there is less likely to be a problem of personalizing the relationship and finding endings a problem. This is an area where good supervision is vital.

OTHER THERAPIES

Most of what we have looked at in the outline of therapies are individual 'talking' therapies. However, there are other types of helping that may benefit the infertile clients, which include group counselling, couple counselling, short-term focused therapy and the creative therapies.

Group Counselling

Group work began in Britain and America around the time of World War II. It was pioneered by Lewin who worked initially with T or Training groups. Carl Rogers also became involved with therapeutic group work. In Britain much of the early, and still well regarded, work was done by Bion at the Tavistock Clinic and by the Mill Hill group of psychiatrists and psychotherapists. They began to identify group dynamics or the 'life' of groups and the shared features of groups of all kinds.

Groups for those with fertility difficulties may be self-help groups, task-centred or therapeutic groups. They share common features and all have some value. This value is not just in the cost/time benefit for the counsellor of seeing several people at one time, but in the support and strength some individuals can gain from their participation. Self-help groups are established and run by those who share the problem. They may use professionals as advisers but they tend not to have a leader.

The shared experience of self-help groups can offer reassurance and encouragement. They can help participants feel that they are helping each other. At a time when you may feel helpless this is a positive effect. Some people feel more confident as a result of this sharing and it empowers them to act in ways they did not expect of themselves, sometimes as advocates for others or in fund-raising or personal support. The social involvement of the group may help clients to feel less isolated and alone. The mutual trust and acceptance of the group can liberate those who have been keeping a secret for a long time. Task-centred groups are established around a particular problem. They may also be established as campaigning groups. Therapeutic groups are usually led by a trained group worker and may be time limited or open ended but are always seen as there to help the members to make changes in their lives.

Problems in groups

Some clients may feel unsafe in a group. They fear exposure and confrontation and need support individually before they feel able to participate. There are some dangers of groups that good leadership should be able to modify, if not eliminate. The group can be hijacked by one member to solve their own problems. This domination may prevent others from expressing their feelings or taking a role in the group. They may also be concerned that they cannot contain or help this individual. There is also the possibility of scapegoating, i.e. one member becoming the target for group hostility or ridicule. This damages not only the individual but also the whole group, who may be frightened of the group's power to harm. There may also be times when the expression of painful feelings by a group member cannot be dealt with or contained. This can be followed up with an individual session.

Setting up a group

The initiator must decide on the group's purpose. If it is to be self-help then leadership will be largely informal and administrative. If it is to be therapeutic or task-centred there needs to be a trained group leader appointed. Styles of leadership vary from the controlling, via the democratic to the non-leadership style, where the group is left to set its own tasks and agendas and the leader is there to interpret the dynamic. Sometimes it works better to have two leaders who can support and monitor each other. The danger here comes from jealousies or disagreements between the leaders that then destabilize the group. The group needs to be planned: the size, location, frequency of meeting, length of sessions and whether it is a 'closed' or 'open' group, with a free membership. Members also need to be clear about the role of the leader and the resources available. If this is all decided before the start then the initial settling in or negotiating period of the group is reduced in time.

The development of the group

Rogers (1991) and Yalom (1970), as well as other group theorists, identify stages in the life of a group. These begin with the negotiating phase when the group is concerned with rules and procedures. People are finding out about each other and about the leader. Talk is mainly superficial and information giving and seeking. The next stage often produces conflict as the group begins to sort out roles and levels of commitment and power. This may actually serve to unite the group to move into stage three, which is one of community and sharing. The purpose of the group is understood and there is trust and confidence established. The next stage of action is when people start to use the group. They listen to and support each other and there is a feeling of connectedness. The final stage is the ending; this may be difficult for some members and they may try to keep it going, by introducing new issues or reactivating old ones. There may be expressions of anxiety and loss that will need to be dealt with individually for some members. Just as in individual therapy, good preparation for the ending can ease the sense of loss.

Couple Therapy

Working with couples demands as much, if not more, skill than working with individuals. Kennedy (1977) writes 'No counselling has more unexpected turns in it than that involving (couples). It illustrates the amazing and unexpected variety of life as one of the most charming aspects of human nature. People frequently do not do what we think they are going to do, especially when they are married to each other. Such peculiar discoveries teach us not to be overconfident in our own judgement about what other people should or might do. Some married people are willing to settle for less or for only a bit more than we think they should get or deserve from life'.

The counsellor has to be particularly aware of their own experiences, expectations and prejudices around relationships in order to help the clients. Everyone has their own ideas about how to run a relationship and their fantasies about how other people run theirs. One of the great pitfalls of couple counselling is taking sides. This may be as a result of seeing one of the couple first and establishing a relationship with them, or from the effects of transference and counter-transference or from the unconscious seduction by one of the couple to have the counsellor on their side. The counsellor needs to be aware of, and working with, all these issues.

If both partners are willing to attend for counselling, the therapist will have to decide whether to see them always together, sometimes together or always separately. If only one is seen for help then there is the danger of what Kennedy refers to as the 'sick-one, healthy-one' relationship, where the partner who is receiving help is blamed for all the difficulties of the couple. The decision whether to see them together may be their choice or reflect how comfortable the helper is with working with them together. At times when there is a high information input into the session, seeing them together is important. This eliminates the fantasy that one has all the information and therefore more power. Joint sessions also help the couple to 'hear' each other, to listen to the other's version of the story and the expression of feelings. Where they have become protective of each other it may be difficult for them to talk about all their feelings and this needs some skill on the part of the counsellor to make it as safe a place as possible.

It can be helpful where there is some maladaptive pattern of behaviour or the relationship seems out of balance for the counsellor to help the couple work through this together. The helper must listen to the feelings not just to the problems, and understand and express an understanding of those feelings to each individual.

It must be remembered that couples will not change or grow at the same rate. They may find change in the other difficult to accept, even when they want the change to occur, and it can feel threatening to their relationship. Couples may produce problems that the counsellor does not feel able to help with. This is especially true of sexual dysfunction and psychosexual problems. The counsellor should then discuss with the clients whether they will be better helped elsewhere and how that referral should be made.

Short-term or Focused Interventions

Short-term work has been shown to be effective and positive. Even Freud used some short-term work in his analysis, but most of the development has come later. In Britain, Balint and Malan, both working at the Tavistock Clinic, have developed the theories and practice of short-term therapeutic work.

It may be necessary to work short-term because of cost, staff shortages or pressure of client numbers. Sometimes it may be led by the clients who do not want longer-term work. Even in one session people can be helped to clarify their thinking and approach a problem in a different way. Two conditions are essential for effective short-term work: there must be a focus to the work and the client must be motivated to work hard in the sessions. The focus may be discussed between the counsellor and client, with the understanding that as the work progresses they may need to accept that there is another focus more appropriate to the client's needs. Mann (1979) believes that four core issues emerge regularly for clients:

- independence vs. dependence
- activity vs. passivity
- adequate self-esteem vs. loss of self-esteem
- unresolved loss or delayed grief.

These areas can all be the focus of the work and the client and therapist may choose to work at the here-and-now level or to explore past experiences in the light of present difficulty.

Malan (1981) and Davanloo (1979), who have researched and written extensively about short-term interventions, believe that the therapist has to be quite interpretative and use transference actively. Davanloo is particularly confrontational in his work, which may not suit all counsellors. However, the important principle is the need to remain focused and not stray into other problem areas that the client may raise. It is also important to keep the boundaries very clear. The client will be dealing with the loss of the therapist very early in the work. This may provoke helpful issues around loss and letting go but will also need to be addressed by the counsellor at the beginning of the contact.

Cognitive-analytic therapy (CAT) is also used as a short-term treatment. It involves the therapist helping the client to identify and understand areas of difficulty in cognition or thinking, with the therapist working alongside the client in a time-limited framework to effect change.

There is good evidence that short-term focused work does produce change for the client that they are able to take into all areas of their life. It enables the client to set a goal and feel they have achieved some change, which is encouraging and empowering.

Creative Therapies

Art, drama, dance and music are all used for therapeutic purposes. These non-verbal techniques help the clients to express their needs and feelings, when words seem inadequate or inappropriate. It often opens a new world for people who have not considered themselves creative or ever tried to express themselves in paint or movement. The therapist does not allow it to become concerned with the perfection of the product but the value of the process and the effect of the self-awareness that it can produce. Regan Wright, an art therapist writing in *Supportive Therapies in Health Care* (Wells and Tschudin 1994) says 'Therapy should be an open-ended situation in which patients or clients have the maximum opportunity to find their own direction and therefore to build self-awareness and insight on their own terms'.

Creative work can be liberating and fun but also a place where people can get in touch with fear and pain. It may, for some, be a safe way to express feelings, away from the threat of danger and damage in one-to-one relationships with a therapist. The work can be private or shared with the therapist or a group. The use of art and drama therapy for clients with infertility problems in particular is explained in *Infertility Counselling* edited by Sue Jennings (1995).

There are many ways of trying to help clients to understand and cope with their problems; they are all effective some of the time and with some people. We can perhaps best remember that 'the role of the counsellor is to facilitate the client's work in ways which respect the client's values, personal resources and capacity for self-determination' (British Association for Counselling 1992).

REFERENCES

Berne, E. (1964) *Transactional Analysis in Psychotherapy*, London: Souvenir Press.

British Association for Counselling (1992) *Code of Practice*, Rugby, Warwickshire: BAC.

Carkuff, R. (1987) *The Art of Helping*, Amherst: Human Resources Development Press.

Davanloo, H. (1979) *Short Term Dynamic Psychotherapy*, Aronson.

Egan, G. (1986) *The Skilled Helper*, Southampton: Brooks/Cole Monterey.

Ellis, A. (1990) *Reason and Emotion in Psychotherapy*, New York: Citadel Press.

Jennings, S. (Ed.) (1995) *Infertility Counselling*, Oxford: Blackwell.

Kennedy, E. and Charles, S.C. (1977) *On Becoming a Counsellor*, Dublin: Gill and Macmillan.

Malan, D. (1981) *The Frontiers of Brief Psychotherapy*, New York: Plenum Press.

Mann, J. (1979) *Time Limited Psychotherapy*, Boston: Harvard University Press.

Maslow, A. (1968) *Towards a Psychology of Being*, 2nd edn, Toronto: Van Nostrand.

Perls, F. (1969) *The Gestalt Approach and Eye Witness to Therapy*, New York: Bantam.

Rogers, C. (1991) *Client-centred Therapy,* London: Constable.

Wells, R. and Tschudin V. (Eds) (1994) *Supportive Therapies in Health Care*, London: Baillière Tindall.

Yalom, I. (1970) *The Theory and Practice of Group Psychotherapy*, New York: Basic Books.

Chapter 5

Who Can Be the Counsellor?

In many health settings the person who counsels does not necessarily wear the official label 'counsellor'. Patients in distress take their troubles to those who seem able to understand and offer support and common sense, those who seem available and approachable. Thus the perception of the clients or patients may determine who is the counsellor or at least who is asked to offer counsel.

The staff themselves may see this as their role or feel that no one else is fulfilling it and that the needs of the clients are going unmet. Many doctors and nurses in this situation are concerned that they may not be doing the 'right thing', and are very conscious of their lack of training in counselling, and fear they are operating from what Levant called 'a smattering of ignorance'.

A further perception of who can be the counsellor may come from the institution itself. Encouraged or required to offer 'counselling', there may be pressure for an identified person to fill that role regardless of their suitability or expertise. Counselling is, unfortunately, sometimes seen as something anyone can do if they have the time and they show some interest. However, counselling requires two elements to be present to be effective: the personal qualities of the counsellor and the acquisition of skills within a theoretical framework. It is possible to offer what may be called a counselling approach to helping clients that is not seen by either counsellor or client as a therapeutic experience, as may be offered in psychotherapy or formal counselling, but a way of helping them to examine their situation and provide appropriate support and information that the client can make use of in decision-making and which helps to reduce the stress involved in the processes and procedures of infertility treatment.

THE OFFICIAL REQUIREMENTS

The HFEA Code of Practice (1990) recommends three distinct types of counselling that should be available to clients and are recognized as beneficial. These are implications counselling, support counselling and therapeutic counselling. The King's Fund Centre Counselling Committee's Report on Counselling for Regulated Infertility Treatments (1991) also includes a recommendation that information counselling is available.

- *Implications counselling* is the exploration of the personal and family implications of treatments including gamete donation. This requires skilled counselling by someone well informed about the medical aspects of treatment.
- *Support counselling* is the provision of support throughout the time of contact with the clinic and may be offered by any staff member.
- *Therapeutic counselling* is a treatment process 'focusing on healing, on the gradual adjustment of expectations and the eventual acceptance of life circumstances'. This requires either skilled counsellors in the clinic or the clients can be referred elsewhere.
- *Information counselling* is the provision of information, advice and discussion that can be offered by any member of the clinic's team.

Legally there is a responsibility to offer access to counselling but no obligation to provide it in any particular form or to control who is the counsellor.

The service that the counsellor should provide is more clearly set down than who is to provide it and often the role is combined with that of the nurse. The nurse/counsellor is an increasingly valuable role in health services, offering the opportunity for patients to have access to counselling services that would either be unavailable to them or very costly and including the expertise that many clients feel is a vital part of counselling for infertility. The patient may already perceive the nurse as having information and an interest and concern for their state of mind as well as their health. There may also be an assumption of professional ethics such as confidentiality and trust. Thus the HFEA recommendations of offering counselling for information, implications and support may be perceived by the patient as an extension of the nurse's role. The nurse may feel that she/he needs more specific training and support to offer any of these, in particular the fourth element, therapeutic counselling. There may be some concern that the nurse or doctor who is involved with intimate physical care of the patient may have some difficulty in transferring to the counselling role; or that the person who is giving information or taking a formal medical history may not be able to step into the more emotional relationship required of the counsellor. It may be useful to examine this by looking at the personal requirements of the effective counsellor and the difficult areas that counsellors encounter in their work.

PERSONAL QUALITIES OF THE COUNSELLOR

Self-awareness

The most important quality for a counsellor to possess is self-awareness. It allows us to work in the very stressful area of people's pain and distress – to be able to be 'with' a client without taking on their pain for ourselves and becoming so identified with that person that we can no longer help them. Self-awareness helps us to develop what are called ego boundaries. They mark the edges of ourselves and help us to recognize the client as a separate person with separate problems. If we do not have these boundaries and we make the other person an extension of ourselves, we may project our own problems or solutions onto the client and not be able to 'hear' what the client is telling us about their situation. If we do not have a boundary between ourselves and the client, we may feel that the client has the same problems as us and that our solutions may be the answer to their problem. Clients may see the counsellor as someone who is successful and has no problems and is therefore very susceptible to suggestions that worked for him or her.

Recognizing how you work, what motivates you, pleases you and angers you and what your needs are, frees you to listen to others. Recognizing what is happening in your own emotional and psychic state is the first step in being able to deal with it and not let it affect the relationship with the client. It is within this relationship that the work of the counsellor is done. Carl Rogers (1951) wrote, 'If I can form a helping relationship to myself – if I can be sensitively aware of an acceptance towards my own feelings . . . then the likelihood is great that I can form a helping relationship towards another'.

The relationship with the client, as the central part of the work involves the concepts of transference and counter-transference. *Transference* refers to the feelings of the client towards those helping them. These feelings belong to past relationships that were important in their lives, especially with parents. Thus the counsellor may become viewed as the parent, both positively and negatively. If the counsellor is not aware of being put in the role of the good parent, they may begin to play this role and little progress can be made in the counselling. The counsellor may also begin to feel too involved without recognizing what has happened and want to withdraw from the relationship, possibly confirming previous damaging parental behaviour. *Counter-transference* refers to the feelings, positive or negative, that the helper feels towards the client. These come from our own previous experience and our needs. We may be strongly attracted to, or repelled by, the client's presentation and we need to pay attention to these feelings and understand that they are not part of the work we are doing. Supervision and training help the counsellor to remain conscious of the dangers and benefits of transference and counter-transference.

Self-awareness is not self-consciousness, that uncomfortable feeling of everyone looking at you and judging you, but rather consciousness of self. It is the awareness of our outer self and physical body and our emotional and spiritual inner self and how they are integrated. Learning self-awareness must come from looking inward to examine honestly our thought processes, belief systems and feelings and also from feedback from others, learning to accept and value how other people perceive us. This learning is often best done in a group; it can be painful as well as instructive, helping us to become more aware of our ability to communicate, verbally and non-verbally. As counsellors, we need to be conscious of not just the words we say but what we do not say and how we convey both. Clients will be aware of our bodies as well as our words, so we need to be aware of them too.

Other-awareness

Egan (1982) gave this portrait of a helper: 'They respect their clients and express this respect by being available to them, working with them, not judging them, trusting the constructive forces found in them, and ultimately placing the expectation on them that they will do whatever is necessary to handle the problems in living more effectively'.

Carl Rogers (1951) believed that all the conditions for effective counselling stem from what he called 'unconditional positive regard'. The skills discussed in Chapter 4 are based on this concept and it may be helpful to examine more closely Rogers' definition:

> *'I hypothesise that growth and change are more likely to occur the more the counsellor is experiencing a warm, positive, acceptant attitude towards what is the client. It means that he prizes his client, as a person ... It means he cares for his client in a non-possessive way, as a person with potentialities ... It respects the other person as a separate individual and does not possess him. It is a kind of liking which has strength, and is not demanding'.*

Carkuff (1969) and Rogers (1951) identified the qualities of the self-aware counsellor as warmth, genuineness and empathy.

105

Warmth

Burnard (1989) describes warmth as a frame of mind rather than a skill. Self-awareness gives us a regard for our place in the world that allows us to respect the other person as an equal, non-judgementally and non-defensively. Warmth is the quality that gives us a recognition of the differences and the conditions for respect and acceptance. It may be easier to conceive of it as the opposite of coldness, which would not encourage a client to trust or relate to the counsellor. The warm relationship is not friendship or even perhaps an equal relationship. The counselling alliance is not an equal relationship – the client has come to the counsellor asking for help and expecting expertise – but the relationship will be most effective when the client is valued as an equal.

Genuineness

Real interest in the client is vital to the counselling relationship. We cannot expect to like all our clients and that is not part of genuineness. It is the interest in what is happening within the relationship where genuine concern will progress the counselling. Genuineness is present in the counsellor who is open and not defensive; consistent and congruent. This congruence is the 'match' between beliefs, behaviour and thoughts and our expression of those thoughts. The smile that reaches the eyes feels congruent, whereas body language that expresses boredom whilst the words express interest is seen by the client as lack of honesty and trust is destroyed.

Empathy

Rogers (1951) has this definition of empathy: 'it is the ability to perceive the internal frame of reference of another with accuracy, and with the emotional components and meaning which pertain thereto, as if one were the other person, but without ever losing the "as if" condition'. It is the ability to enter the world of the other person and to convey this identification. It is not sympathy, which is feeling sorry for someone, and can be felt from a distance.

It again refers back to the safety of the self-aware counsellor, who feels able to embark on a journey alongside the client, without their own defences preventing them from entering the other's world. The client may experience this empathy from the understanding displayed by the counsellor and the ability to listen and hear. The reflective technique referred to in Chapter 4 may help in this understanding. A deeper level of empathy, as explained by Carkuff (1969), is where the counsellor begins to use intuition and interpretation.

THE LIMITATIONS OF COUNSELLING

Who can be the counsellor may be in part defined by the limits of the situation, the clients or the counsellor.

The Situation

To offer effective counselling we must be able to offer time and space. It may not be important to offer the 'therapeutic hour' (usually 50 minutes!) but we must have time given just to that client, the limits of which are clarified. If the client is told they have half an hour, they are clear about how much they may want to start talking about or it may seem ample time to find out information or examine a problem. When they are offered that time it has to be their time. It is difficult to feel valued if the time you have is interrupted by telephones or bleeps, or by someone knocking on the door. The space also needs to feel comfortable. Again the client is not encouraged to think that their problems are important if the counsellor has to wander around looking for an empty space, or perching on a desk somewhere. The client also needs to be aware of the boundaries of confidentiality. If the counsellor feels that information may need to be shared with the whole team, then the client should be aware of this. It gives them the choice of what they discuss with the counsellor and creates a feeling of trust. Similarly with notes; clients are usually aware that there are medical notes and letters to GPs and need to know whether their counselling sessions will be included in the medical notes or recorded elsewhere. They also need to know whether they have access to them. All this contributes to a feeling of some control over the situation for the client in an area of their lives where they already feel quite powerless. Access to counselling should also be made clear: whether they can contact the counsellor out of clinic hours, whether the counsellor will be available to them throughout their treatment and if the counsellor is prepared to see them after treatment, whether the outcome is successful or not. It may also make the counselling relationship more equal if the client can be helped to understand the agenda of the agency, who they will see at what stage of treatment and how information about them may be passed around the team and outside of it. This again helps the client to feel less at the mercy of agents outside themselves and more in control.

The Clients

Not all clients will want to take advantage of counselling. This may be as a result of their image of counselling, their previous experience or how the offer is presented to them.

Many people feel that counselling is for those who are not coping, for the 'mad' or the bad. Several of the people we spoke to who had attended clinics said that they were unwilling to take up the offer of counselling as they felt it labelled them, that they would be pleased 'to talk to someone' but shied away from the word counselling. They may have no experience of it, not just as a way of exploring feelings and helping to make decisions but on a more basic level of being a way of obtaining information and having questions answered. The way in which counselling is presented may help to overcome some of these barriers. If it is regarded by the clinic as something that is offered to all patients as part of the service then there is no stigma attached. If someone is making the assessment of who needs it, this should be the counsellor, who is most likely to know what they are being offered and can outline the range of help and advice available. If people have had bad experiences of counselling in the past, which were unhelpful or even harmful, it may be possible to ask another team member to talk to the client, offering some of the same service as the counsellor with the counsellor's support and guidance if necessary. A few clients are regarded as not amenable to counselling; these include those who have clear mental illness, particularly psychosis, and the suicidal, although some experienced counsellors are willing and able to support them.

The Counsellor

We are all limited: by our motivation, skills, experience and training, by time and just because we are human.

Motivation

Most counsellors counsel because they care. They can understand or have experienced themselves that people can be helped by the process. This caring is essential, but so is a clear idea of why you are counselling. It is not for solving problems or making things better although this may be part of the result. Looking for 'success' may actually make the counselling less effective. If we become too involved with the clients and their pain and wanting to make everything all right, it may lead to us finding it difficult to end the counselling when it is appropriate or to confront situations within the process which we fear may result in the client not liking us. Dealing with hostility or anger becomes very threatening if we have personalized the relationship.

Over-involvement or over-work can also lead to burnout, the loss of interest or energy for the work or cynicism and distancing. This can be the result of repeatedly working with the same problem so that the 'story' becomes so familiar that we lose sight of the individual; from a feeling of the need to produce results or success (in the health care field this may come from colleagues who do not understand the counselling process and just want us to make the patients feel better); or from lack of support or supervision and from unresolved personal conflicts and issues. Too little involvement with the clients leads to no change, boredom for the counsellor or a move into simple advice-giving, when this is not what is required or expected by the clients.

Hilary had worked as a qualified nurse/counsellor in a clinic attached to a gynaecology department for several years. She enjoyed the work,

109

which provided some variety of referrals and a mix of clients. She says, 'I was never really supported by my medical colleagues, two of them certainly had little time for counselling. They used the service to calm down the anxious and the tearful and for services that the hospital required counselling input, such as termination of pregnancy. The nursing and midwifery staff were more supportive and regularly referred women to me but had little time to discuss the clients or their progress. I struggled for a while feeling angry with people who did not appreciate what I did or what services could be offered that the patients did value. I began to feel less interested in the work and that I was not really taking the interest in the clients that I had in the past. I talked this over with my supervisor eventually; it took a while because I felt that it was the system and nothing to do with my work. My supervisor began by looking at the lack of feedback from the work. Many clients only attended for one session and there was no follow-up. She felt that I was mostly advice and information giving and doing a superficial assessment'. Hilary realized that she had to make a change and tried to expand the work that she could do within the department if she was not to lose her skills and her motivation for the job. She offered to do one session a week with the subfertility clinic and some with another hospital team. 'I was having to convince them of the value of counselling and I suppose that it made me think more about the value and also the way I worked, in having to "sell" myself I was selling the work too.' She found this gave her the opportunity to offer more than one session and to follow some of the clients throughout their treatment. The work was appreciated by the team and Hilary felt valued and more interested in the work.

Skills

These skills are examined in detail in Chapter 4. They are always limiting us in counselling because we can always learn and develop. This does not need to prevent us from doing good work; it just means we can always be better. We learn from our colleagues, from training, supervision, from co-counselling or support networks and always from our clients.

Experience and training

Training helps to build on personal abilities to develop the skills we need to become competent as counsellors and to extend into particular areas. For those who counsel in infertility there is an expressed need from the clients to have someone who is familiar with the medical causes and treatments as well as having good counselling skills. Training and experience helps the counsellor to feel more confident and to avoid some of the pitfalls of counselling that have been discussed above. Whatever the school of counselling that has formed the basis of training the counsellor has undergone, simply to have a theoretical basis gives the counsellor a way of approaching the work and a means of evaluating its progress and usefulness.

Time

The limitations of time are very real; they are not just set by the institution but also by the counsellor and the client. If they are made clear from the beginning and repeated during the contact there is less danger of them becoming a damaging factor. No-one feels so abandoned at the end of sessions or the end of contact with the counsellor if they have been clear throughout that this would end, and the counsellor has known when it was appropriate to start dealing with the client's feelings about endings. This also applies to individual session times. Good work can be done in one session as well as in extended therapy if the focus is there. There has been increasing interest in short-term focused therapy (see Chapter 4).

Being human

We are all limited by what we can do at any one time. We may feel tired unwell or low, or we may have personal conflicts with which we need to deal. All this takes energy from the work. If it seems to be too demanding, we may need to take some time away from counselling. Sometimes when we are dealing with a personal issue, it will take over the feelings we are experiencing from the clients. It is easy to see a particular problem as theirs when it really belongs to us. Good supervision and support can help us through this, and being aware of it may be enough to help us focus on the work and the clients not on the problem. If not, then it is not a failure to take time for yourself; it is a success to recognize it and take the right action.

THE GENDER OF THE COUNSELLOR

There may not be a choice about who can counsel a client, male or female, but where there is a possibility of same-sex counselling this may need to be considered by the team. There seems little evidence that men or women make better counsellors and it is more a function of their personal qualities. Women are often regarded as more naturally nurturing and less confrontational and this may affect the client's perception. Some feminist counsellors also believe that women's shared experience of their expected role and position in society makes counselling between women more effective. However, it is generally how the counsellor relates to the client that will be a measure of how effective the work can be, rather than their gender. There may be some areas of fertility counselling when gender is more important. Some people can feel uncomfortable talking about sexual matters with a counsellor of the opposite sex, although this may be more of a problem in thought than in reality. Most counsellors who work in infertility agree that if the counsellor is professional and empathic in their approach this is not a difficulty, except for some clients from ethnic groups who would not consider discussing these matters with a member of the opposite sex. What may be more important is that the counsellor of either gender has an understanding of the different needs of men and women in relation to their infertility and at different stages of the treatment process. Women are often more comfortable with sharing thoughts and feelings and being encouraged to explore their internal world. This may be with the counsellor and/or with other women. It seems from experience and talking to many women that they need to pay attention to feelings of loss and grieving throughout the time of diagnosis and treatment. This need may be thought to be less acute for men but they are concerned about loss of self-esteem and the connection between fertility and virility, particularly at the beginning of treatment. They have a feeling of unfairness and also of uselessness, which they find hard to share with men friends who may joke about it or minimize its importance. Equally they may transfer this to feeling that it is difficult to share this with a male counsellor. Many men find it hard to be in touch with feelings of sadness and loss and easier to contact anger and threat. Their cultural or family background may make it hard for them to express these powerful feelings to a woman, and this may need to be explored as part of the therapy.

It may be best for the counsellor to encourage the discussion about other-gender counselling during the initial contact with the client.

TRANS-CULTURAL COUNSELLING

When working with patients seeking help with problems of infertility we have to be particularly sensitive to the client's understanding and feelings about being childless, about seeking medical help and about the gender of those treating them, within their religious and cultural background. We need to have information and awareness of different attitudes to sex, contraception and fertility. Whilst the dominant white culture is encouraged to consider contraception, many religious groups including Catholics and orthodox Jews do not practise contraception, and often regard their proven fertility as part of their standing in society. Infertility for some ethnic groups may be seen as a punishment, thus inducing guilt and suspicion. Who they are prepared to talk to about this may be affected by their perceptions of the counsellor and also the way that counselling is offered.

It is often not possible to match client and counsellor for race and cultural experience. It is more important to develop the skills to relate to the client's needs rather than fit resources to the clients. Where this happens there is an understanding of their feelings, fears and expectations which can override difficulties of cultural learning and experience.

It is possible to do effective counselling work with clients of another race or culture but it does demand an awareness of differences and of our own prejudices. It may be helpful to both client and counsellor to acknowledge the differences at the beginning of contact. This may be in something as simple as how someone is addressed and the pronunciation of a name. If the counsellor is ignorant of some aspects of the client's cultural or religious experience he or she may be able to ask the client for information. Where this feels unhelpful to the client or there are language barriers to understanding, then it may be possible to find support from within their own ethnic group or for the counsellor to be able to seek advice and information. An honest expression of the lack of knowledge or understanding may help to enable the client and counsellor to work together. We all have prejudices; it is how aware we are of preventing them from becoming a negative part of our counselling work that will stop them being harmful to the clients. This is true of class and religion as well as colour and culture. We have to be aware as counsellors of how we are relating to a client all the time and to examine transference and counter-transference. This is particularly true when we are working cross-culturally. If we are aware of the prejudices of others it may be necessary to confront these, if the client is not to receive a poor or discriminatory service.

Gita, a 32-year-old Indian woman, approached her GP about her problems conceiving. She had experienced a miscarriage 6 years previously and this had been her only pregnancy, despite not using contraception since her marriage. She lived with her husband, an accountant, and her parents-in-law, who owned several businesses. She worked for her father-in-law as a secretary. She was very close to her own parents and *siblings but had never established a good relationship with her husband's mother whom she felt was critical and domineering. Her two sisters-in-law both had children and the grandparents lavished gifts and attention on their grandchildren. Gita's childlessness was referred to by all the family. Gita felt very depressed at her failure to conceive and broke down in tears with the doctor. She was referred to the practice counsellor, a middle-aged Welsh woman.* 'I was so pleased to be able to cry about it, that at first that was all I seemed to do. For the first two sessions I just cried. I needed her to understand how much it mattered to me. But not just to me, to my whole family. I think it probably took longer to get her to understand this; just how involved the whole family were in my being pregnant. She seemed to find it hard to understand that I could not assert myself with my mother-in-law, as my husband would have been very upset by this and much of our way of life would have been under threat. It would sometimes have helped to have someone who understood the significance of a child and I sometimes felt I was wasting the short time we had. But I also realized that in explaining what it was like to go to a big family wedding and what it was like to be part of a whole tradition, not just a family, it made it clear for me too. The part I did find difficult was that my husband really wanted nothing to do with the treatment; he did not think it was his problem and this affected not just how he thought about me but how the whole family regarded me and how I felt about myself. I think on the whole it would have been easier to have an Indian woman counsellor but the woman I saw was open and warm and that was important to me. I couldn't have talked to a man though.'*

115

SUPERVISION

The Code of Practice of the British Association for Counselling (BAC) requires that all counsellors should receive supervision on a regular basis, the primary purpose of which is 'to ensure that the counsellor is addressing the needs of the client'. Supervision is a vital part of the counsellor's ongoing learning, providing for support, evaluation and skills development. It also offers help in difficult areas such as ethics, dealing with transference and counter-transference, and decisions about who might benefit from counselling and when to end sessions. It is not usually involved with the personal needs of the counsellor.

In that the basis of supervision is the needs of the client, how much expertise the supervisor should have in a particular area of work may be an important issue for the counsellor. Whether someone working in infertility needs to have a supervisor who has expertise in the field or is merely an experienced counsellor may be for that individual to decide. In a specialized area of work it may be difficult to find a supervisor who has the expertise, and it may be more important to find the right person for you, or perhaps someone who has experience in dealing with medico-social problems, and is aware of the constraints and advantages of working within a medically based team. Support in the particular area of infertility may be provided by the team finding a formalized way of discussing client needs, i.e. peer group supervision or offering co-supervision with other team members.

Peer group supervision involves several counsellors sharing responsibility for supervising each other. This is most effective and appropriate where the counsellors are of fairly equal experience and status, and without managerial responsibility for others in the group.

Co-supervision involves two counsellors alternating the role of supervisor and counsellor, dividing the time equally between them.

Supervision for Personal Issues

Whilst supervision is not intended to, and should not, replace personal counselling or therapy, it should be used to help the counsellor identify areas of their personality and practice that may affect their work.

The personal qualities of the counsellor are an integral and perhaps the most important part of what makes a good counsellor. Their ability to listen and hear, to attend to the client and to hold painful information and feelings, makes them effective and able to help the client move towards living in a more satisfying way. These personal qualities include the counsellor's own feelings and prejudices, experiences and doubts. It is part of self-awareness that they are not taken into the counselling process, but it is important for the counsellor to be aware of them. We all hold some prejudices and we need to be conscious of them if they are not to impede the work or at worst be harmful to the client. When working in infertility it is important that the counsellor has a clear idea of their own feelings about fertility and parenting, about gender differences in attitudes to parenting and about loss and bereavement. If the counsellor is carrying their own feelings there can be a pressure for the client to confirm or collude with those prejudices or it may be difficult for the counsellor to hear and allow feelings that he or she sees to be wrong or negative. If the counsellor is holding negative feelings about a particular ethnic or religious group, those again may harm or impede the work. Being honest with oneself and using the supervisory process to examine feelings helps to minimize the damage that may be done, albeit unconsciously.

TRAINING AND QUALIFICATIONS

Those who call themselves counsellors should have some formal training in counselling skills from a recognized institution. This training will vary in length and theoretical framework from one training organization to another, but all will have addressed the basic principles of counselling and the skills required for effective work. Training is available at many colleges and universities as well as private regulated therapy institutes. The courses last from 1 to 4 years and may be full- or part-time. The students will be required not just to study and write about theoretical aspects of therapy and counselling skills but also to be involved in regular work as a trainee with clients under supervision. There may also be large and small groups which will be intended to help the counsellor's personal development. Many courses also require the students to be in therapy themselves for at least part of the course.

Membership of the British Association for Counselling is not an indication of qualification but there is an expectation that members will adhere to their Code of Ethics and Practice. Accreditation by the BAC is a measure of experience and training. There are, however, many well trained and experienced counsellors who have not sought accreditation. It is important that anyone consulting or employing a counsellor should be aware of the training they have received, that they work to a Code of Practice and that they are being supervised. Ongoing training in specialized areas of counselling or to achieve further qualifications is also available (see Appendix).

Specific training for infertility counselling is developing but as yet there are no clear guidelines of what should be taught and levels of competency for teaching and no body setting standards. The Working Group on Training for Infertility Counselling was set up to consider how training for those involved in infertility counselling might be developed. As well as general counselling skills and good practice, which would be included on any accredited counselling course, they recommended that training should cover:

- the needs of people affected by infertility and those donating gametes or acting as surrogate mothers
- child and family issues relating to children born as a result of assisted conception
- an understanding of the treatment on assisted conception programmes and options to treatment
- training and career paths for the staff involved.

This would meet the identified needs outlined in the Working Party document to improve standards and develop a body of knowledge and good practice.

REFERRING ON

There may be times when it is appropriate to refer a client to another counsellor or other professional. This may be for an expert opinion such as a psychiatric or medical referral, or to a counsellor who works in a different way or has an area of particular interest or expertise. Clients who are initially referred for problems concerned with fertility may want to explore other issues once counselling has begun. It is important then for the counsellor to be able to negotiate with the client whether they would be better to see another helper, perhaps after finishing sessions with the fertility counsellor, or whether they would feel let down by a change. It may then be necessary for the counsellor to seek support and advice elsewhere, to enable them to help the client.

Moira and Justin had married in their twenties and wanted to start a family very quickly. When they did not get pregnant Moira did not want to wait long and was referred by her GP to the infertility clinic after 8 months. A history of salpingitis was suspicious of tubal damage and this was confirmed by laparoscopy. Moira had suspected this may be the case and was eager to start IVF. After the first attempt she had a positive pregnancy test but started to bleed a few days later. Moira was devastated and Justin did not know how to cope with Moira or his own feelings. Counselling was offered to give them a space to bring their pain and to identify their different needs. Justin felt that in his (Jamaican) background he was able to feel 'what will be, will be' and demonstrated a relaxed attitude that infuriated Moira. Moira needed to deal with her own feelings as well, but it took her some time to feel comfortable with the counselling sessions. She saw the counsellor as part of the clinic's team. She felt worried about bringing her

119

> *psychological self into the sessions, fearing that it would prejudice the offer of further treatment if she revealed doubts or especially anger. She needed issues of boundaries and confidentiality very clearly defined before she felt able to express and explore her deep anger and pain.*

Some clients may benefit from group sessions as well as or instead of individual counselling. These offer a forum for discussion and sharing that may feel less threatening for some clients than individual sessions, allowing them to listen and observe, without having to talk about themselves until they are ready. There are areas of therapeutic group work that require particular expertise (see Chapter 4), but support groups run by the clinic or the clients themselves can be very positive and valuable.

The nurse/counsellor may be in the position of having to decide whether an involvement with the medical treatment of the client is a problem in particular cases. Again the issue of boundaries and confidentiality is important if the client is to feel 'safe' with the counsellor.

> *Joy had worked at an infertility clinic for 3 years and found her role as a nurse/counsellor rewarding. She was aware that she had to make clear boundaries for her clients about what counselling offered if they were to benefit from counselling. Many clients saw her first in her role as a nurse and for some that was how she remained. 'It is difficult to decide when it is appropriate not to answer medical questions that arise in the middle of a counselling session, like "can I have treatment next month". Your mind automatically starts to look at whether it is possible, when you should be concentrating back on the client and what is going on for her and whether this is a request for approval or the raising of an important issue for her. Once I*

have started seeing someone for counselling, I need to consider if it is appropriate for me to be involved at all in their medical treatment. It can be confusing for both the client and myself. There is always the possibility that the client wishes to use me as an advocate, to show the medical team that she is really being good. In that scenario any useful work could possibly be sabotaged and so this would need addressing early on in the counselling.

Being involved with treatment you are concerned with the provision of a good service. If the clinic views much of its success in terms of pregnancy rates it may be difficult to stay focused on the client and their needs, which may be to choose not to start treatment or to end before a pregnancy. I have known women to ask for a termination after IVF treatment and that was a very difficult area to work in. Failure can become a personal issue in terms of medical treatment letting the patient down. It is vitally important to have good supervision to ensure that you remain focused on the client.'

Counselling may not only be offered by an individual. Many of the clients we talked to had received a great deal of advice support and 'good counsel' from local groups and nationwide organizations such as Issue. The particular value of groups for infertile couples or for lesbian women is the sharing of feelings with people who can be expected to share some of the same thoughts and experiences. It was often the first place that people felt free to say how they really felt, to express their doubts and to ask for help. Some felt that they could be 'normal' as part of the group and they would not be judged or expected to explain the situation. Many groups and national organizations have also acted very effectively as pressure groups to expand or demand local and national services for the infertile and to keep those in a position to make changes aware of the problems of infertile people.

121

The person who can be the counsellor is the one who has the personal qualities, the skills, training and motivation to help the client. They need knowledge and understanding of the medical and the psychological process of infertility diagnosis, treatment and decision-making, and an ability to stay with a client through a difficult, painful and life-changing experience.

REFERENCES

Burnard, P. (1989) *Counselling Skills for Health Professionals*, London: Chapman & Hall.

Carkuff, R. (1969) *Helping and Human Relations*, New York: Holt.

Egan, G. (1982) *The Skilled Helper*, 2nd edn, Belmont: Wadsworth.

Human Fertilization and Embryology Authority (1990) *Code of Practice*, London: HFEA.

King's Fund (1991) *Report on Counselling for Regulated Infertility Treatments*, London: King's Fund Centre.

Rogers, C. (1951) *Client-centred Therapy*, Boston: Houghton Mifflin.

Chapter 6

What the Client Wants

INTRODUCTION

In order to reflect accurately what the client wants from the professionals, we sent out postal questionnaires (see Appendix) and recorded telephone and personal interviews. In total we spoke to 45 individuals and couples and 45 questionnaires were returned. Case histories and direct quotes used in this chapter are from these replies and from the authors' experience of working with infertile couples and individuals.

TRYING FOR A BABY

Whilst some couples or individuals start a family by accident or even what they might consider bad luck, most make a decision that the time is right for them. These decisions can be provoked by internal and external factors, including the instinctive drives towards reproduction and the pressure and expectations of society (see Chapter 3). What constitutes 'trying for a baby' may be different for every couple. For most it probably means ending their use of contraception, although some couples never use contraception and for lesbian women and those without sexual partners they may begin by considering assisted conception. Some knowledge of the means of conception may be important. How much is understood about normal reproductive function

123

may depend on the manner and quality of sex education received during school years, when fertility is taken for granted and much time and energy is invested in ensuring a pregnancy does not happen. The emphasis here is on using current contraceptive aids and not learning about the most and least fertile times of the female menstrual cycle. Now the couple want information about fertile periods and attention is paid to becoming pregnant.

Trying to conceive gives focus and can keep a relationship going. The desire to become a parent is experienced more intensely at differing times both within the individual and in the relationship and this may lead to delay in seeking help until both partners realize help is needed. Delay may also be a tactic used by those anxious about the issues raised by parenting. Others find intrusion in such an intimate area unwelcome. The length of time people take before they seek any help with conceiving may reflect on their anxiety about intrusive treatment, their concerns about parenting or their hope that 'everything will be all right'. From our survey people waited for between 6 months and 14 years before seeking professional help.

Nasrin and Joe had been married for 6 years in a stable relationship; both had made good progress in their careers and had a home they felt comfortable with. They decided to stop using contraception, initiated by Nasrin, when she decided not to go for promotion at work. They felt very positive about this decision and were already picking out names and imagining what time of the year the child would be born. They talked a great deal between themselves about the baby and Nasrin told a friend who was 4 months pregnant. They made plans for the future as mothers who could share the experiences of parenting and child-rearing. Neither spoke to their families about the decision to have a baby, although the family was already asking questions. The first few months when her period arrived, Nasrin was disappointed but had ex-

pected it to take some time after she stopped the Pill. They shared feelings about it and began to focus on the best time to have intercourse. Whilst Joe did not find this difficult he began to feel that sex was becoming directed towards pregnancy and spontaneity was being lost. He did not feel able to share these feelings, worrying that this would seem negative and distress Nasrin. As time went on and no pregnancy occurred, Nasrin felt less able to talk about it and started to avoid her friend who had delivered a baby boy. She also began to think that there may be a problem. Were they doing something wrong? Who was to blame? Nasrin decided to attend the Family Planning Clinic as she had been happy seeing them in the past. When she tried to discuss this with Joe, he felt they should just keep trying and not involve anyone else. The clinic suggested that Nasrin have blood tests to check her ovulation and to ask Joe to do a sperm sample. It was now over a year since they had decided to try for a baby. They were now finding it very difficult to talk about a family, both felt guilty about not being able to give the other a child and already felt the sense of loss that came with the feeling that this was now the time when they would have had a child.

BEFORE PROFESSIONAL INVOLVEMENT – WHO TO TELL

Friends, colleagues and family can unknowingly apply pressure and this is often cited as a cause of distress when a pregnancy does not occur. Well-meant questions about the prospects of becoming a grandparent cause much heartache and sadness. The couple want first to acknowledge that there may be a problem within the sanctity of their relationship before exposing their feelings to others. Indeed some choose not to tell parents because they 'Don't want to burden them with the disappointment of never having grandchildren'. When it is decided to tell someone, the person often feels that 'they had no real understanding of what we were going through' and so were unable to offer the support needed.

The work environment may also be another reminder of the failure of fertility. Women think about working in a place where there won't be a lot of young women and somewhere they wouldn't have to stay bright and cheerful, answering questions and 'making it up all the time'. Men do talk together about their families and their children and for those beginning to think that they might have a problem, there is a dawning feeling of sadness of isolation. Philip said 'When Bill told me that he and his partner had just succeeded in becoming pregnant, he also said what a difficult time they had gone through and how long it had taken them. I then felt able to express my anxieties and talk of the problems we were having'.

WHEN TO SEEK PROFESSIONAL INVOLVEMENT

Time scales of how quickly it should happen once the decision has been made to try for a baby differ between the professional view and the client's perception. How long do clients wait before seeking help? In our questionnaire couples waited an average of 18 months but some waited much longer before they felt able to acknowledge that they were experiencing problems. Couples who went to their GP after about 6 months of intercourse without contraception were often told to try for longer or the doctor suggested keeping temperature charts and returning in a few months. Some were satisfied with this and felt that at least they had begun to do something about it; however, others felt that more should be done at this time because they wanted to know if there really was a problem. Some clients who were aware they had medical problems that could affect their fertility were keen to start investigations as soon as possible. These included men and women who had been sterilized, women with endometriosis and those with a history of tubal damage, known ovulatory problems or amenorrhea.

Tina was 35 years old with a job involving a great deal of travelling. She had been with her partner for about a year and they were keen to have a baby. Tina knew that she had several gynaecological operations in her early teens although she was unclear about exactly why. Her mother had died when Tina was 20 and her father had no information about the reasons for her surgery. She felt that she might need to seek help in order to conceive. 'I went to the GP after 6 months trying, in fact I went after the seventh month, 6 months felt like a kind of watershed and I was now justified in seeking help. The GP was quite supportive but felt that I should wait a bit longer. He was not really clear why, but said that most people do get pregnant in the end. I felt that my medical history meant that I was more likely to have problems and it was only after another visit taking my partner with me that the doctor agreed to start the tests.'

In most instances the first professional involvement was with their GP.

ADMITTING THE PROBLEM

Seeing the GP is a public acknowledgement of a private issue. This first professional involvement was vitally important to those who answered the questionnaire. When the GP took them seriously they validated the problem in their eyes and they felt more able to ask 'trivial questions of someone who knew the answers and didn't mind repeating the information'.

Being taken seriously was certainly what many clients wanted and this need was not met in a lot of cases. GPs were found to be 'unsympathetic', 'uninformed' and 'insensitive', particularly where secondary infertility was the problem: 'you've got one child, it will happen again'. This may reflect their experience that pregnancies can occur spontaneously after many years of trying,

127

or personal issues of the GP which they can project either about fertility or parenting.

Common reactions were: 'You need to relax, give yourselves more time – take a holiday – lots of time – you're still young – who needs children anyway!!!!!!'. This leaves the clients feeling more isolated and alone with little real information about whether they have a problem or not.

WHAT CLIENTS WANTED FROM THEIR GP

At this stage clients wanted to be accepted and have a real problem acknowledged so that they could feel free to ask questions. They wanted genuineness and not false reassurance.

Practical issues were of importance and information about investigations and their significance helped them to feel in control. If the GP started investigations it was not always clear whether they had the skills to diagnose correctly the cause of infertility. Those who spent a long time with their GP before referral to a consultant or clinic had uncomfortable feelings about time being wasted. One male respondent to our questionnaire said that he would have liked much more detailed information about the results of the tests and the implications of the results. He felt they were not being given the opportunity to make decisions based on all the information but that they were being 'hurried through' to the next stage with an assumption that this was what they would want.

Many of the replies cited the need for written information about all aspects of diagnosis and treatments. This could then be read and discussed in the privacy of their home and enable appropriate decisions to be made. They wanted to know what they were getting into. It was realized that there was no guarantee of success but knowledge was power.

Issues around availability of treatment, waiting times and choices about treatments were commonly raised. Many used the national self-help groups, which supply leaflets and information. Even at what can be seen as an early stage in infertility, clients are thinking about and want to know more about the most technically advanced methods of fertility treatments.

Alongside the need for medical support, clients had

expectations that they would find space to address feelings. These may be unrealistic given the demands upon the GP but they were left wondering what to do. 'We were left alone with our feelings, our GP could offer medical support but could not deal with feelings.' Infertility is seen as a potential medical problem and the huge emotional issue is discounted. Clients were coping with many anxieties without the chance to reflect on the implications. There was no space to say no – wait – I have doubts; no space to make decisions about what to do next. For some this was the first time they had really talked to each other about what needing to seek help meant for them. This also appeared to raise the issue of what if it never happens?

TREATMENT BY THE GP

The treatment most commonly offered at the surgery would be to stimulate the ovaries of the woman if after investigation she was found to be anovulatory. The most common drug used is clomiphene (see Chapter 2).

REFERRING ON

When and where to refer is often an issue determined by the GP and his or her knowledge of the local or appropriate services available. In some areas GPs are being asked to complete certain blood tests for the woman and semen samples from the man before they refer to an Infertility Clinic. Interpretation of these tests may not be completed until the couple reach the Infertility Clinic so any possible diagnosis will be delayed and the couple are left uncertain without the important information they need to help make the decision about whether they go on or stop any further investigations. They need to consider their willingness to undergo extensive investigative procedures which may be experienced as invasive.

At this stage the client has the opportunity to stop, take stock and in some cases decide to stop permanently or temporarily. They need space to talk together about the future and acknowledge the demands to be made on them as a couple and

129

individually. At the time, the recognition of what diagnosis and treatment will involve leads them to protect their partner from any further anguish and pain and defend themselves from the confirmation of their infertility.

Decisions need to be made about travel to clinics and the financial and time costs involved. This information should be available to them from their GP, or the private clinic to which they have been referred. One client who travelled many miles for treatment found that it was impossible to see the counsellor on the days when she went for a medical consultation or treatment and so she was unable to take up the counselling she wanted.

Some clients felt that the onus to decide was too difficult without having someone to talk it through with, as they were not sure of all the implications involved in making the right choice. Some felt that a counselling approach could offer the space to enable decision-making and then support during treatment in centres far away. This may be the first time that counselling is realistic within the system.

THE CONSULTANT OR CLINIC

The clients visit the clinic or the consultant for two areas of help: diagnosis and treatment. They feel committed at this stage to asking for help to conceive but they may not yet know what that involves in terms of time, money, physiological or psychological demands. Many clients said that they needed clear information about all the areas of diagnosis and treatment. They wanted to know what tests would be performed and the implications of the results for treatment and decision-making. They felt that they were handing over power to the infertility team and were prepared to do so, but in exchange they wanted honesty, commitment and support.

Diagnosis

Clients wanted to have a clear idea of what tests would be done, what they would involve and when they would know the results. If they had already started investigations with the GP they wanted that considered and if the investigations were to be repeated they wanted to know why. They wanted clear explanations of test results and of the procedures to follow. Many felt they had been treated well, having results explained to them in person and time given to answering their questions. However, one couple were told the results of a test for male infertility by letter which concluded 'the only option open to you is donor or adoption'. The couple told us that they then never mentioned the subject again to each other for 2 years. This lack of support when receiving test results was referred to several times; the feelings of failure and loss of hope were hard to bear. 'We were left alone with our feelings, with the despair and anger and not knowing how to talk to each other, how to give each other hope.' 'There was no one to talk to, because obviously when you see the consultant you see him for ten or fifteen minutes, very nice chap, I mean he would answer any questions we had to the best of his ability, but I must admit most the answers were not answers if you see what I mean. You asked him a question and he replied "well it might work it might not work we cannot really say", there were never any clear answers. It sort of feels that there wasn't anyone to hold onto.'

Many couples had still not told other people at this time and were often protecting their parents from the knowledge of their infertility. They felt they had no-one to turn to. Some who had a sympathetic GP found good support there but many felt this was not the role of the GP and did not want to trouble them. One couple said that they particularly felt that 'the onus was put onto us to ask for what help we wanted, we didn't know what was available, we did not want to be labelled as a psychiatric problem – we felt they should have offered us suitable help, not left it to us when we felt confused and sad'.

Most people felt that the psychological effects of diagnosis should be acknowledged; for some it was the first time that it was confirmed they had a problem, and they needed time and support to make choices. A couple from the Midlands felt that they were rushed into decisions about treatment before they had a chance to absorb the news of the diagnosis. 'We felt that they were so keen to offer a solution to the problem that we really had to go along with it. They were doing it all for us but we were still not sure that we wanted it done.' Some people felt that they needed to take some control to ensure that they could make the choice to stop at any time, whilst others felt a strong drive to press ahead to reach a conclusion before they could really look at the choices open to them, not just about treatment but about medical involvement. 'There are other ways that you can solve your problem, your desire to have children, but they didn't consider anything other than medical treatment, that was not even discussed.' This couple started investigations in their twenties, had two miscarriages and then chose adoption as their way of becoming parents.

The value of support groups was emphasized by many of the people we spoke to. They felt free for the first time to talk about their anxieties, to have first-hand reports about treatment options and to feel that they did not need to hide their fears and fantasies.

Continuity of care became an important issue at this stage as people thought about moving into treatment. They wanted to feel that the same staff would be involved and that the whole team cared and were committed to helping. It was not always important which member of staff they discussed it with; it was the approachable manner and caring response that mattered. Some couples made good relationships with the embryologist, whom they felt was really concerned and very connected to their hopes.

Their expectations of counselling at this time were around being given clear information and being given help and support to examine the options for treatment. Several people expressed a strong need for counselling to look at the implications of becoming involved in treatment, the effect it might have on their families, their work and their relationship. They wanted help and encouragement to look beyond the immediate future, not in detail but in general terms. They wanted someone with the knowledge and the skills to help them examine the possibility of not having children or of the need to consider donor insemination or adoption. For the 30% who had no diagnosis they wanted help to understand this, '. . . this uncertainty is hard to bear. Each month there is hope balanced by the knowledge, born out of experience, that there must be a medical problem that has not yet been discovered. Peoples' comments like "if you just relaxed" do not help and increase the feeling that you must be somehow at fault or to blame. Doctors saying such things as "you really should be pregnant by now" make you feel more of a failure'.

Some of the women who already had children felt that their secondary infertility was being minimized, that they should be glad they had a child and that they were not as important. Men who already had children from another relationship were often more relaxed about becoming pregnant but felt it right to support their partners when they recognized that it was very important to them. Some couples dealing with secondary infertility in one partner expressed envy of the partner with the child or children, which they found hard to discuss.

Jacqui was 24 when she met Tom. They started to live together a year later and within 6 months Jacqui suffered a miscarriage. Although distressed by this she felt that she recovered well and intended to wait a few months before trying again. Eight months later Jacqui was pregnant again and delighted. The couple made plans for the baby and bought clothes and toys. Two weeks over dates Jacqui went into labour and the baby girl was stillborn, she was given no explanation for the loss and suffered a severe grief reaction. Tom was very supportive at first but found it hard to deal with his own grief as time went on. Two years later Jacqui felt able to try again for a now longed-for child. She tried for 18 months before consulting her GP and it was nearly 2 years before she was referred for IVF. 'I began to feel very alone with the problem. Almost all my friends as well as my sisters now had children. My mother would say "I thought there might be another chair at the Christmas table this year" and I felt terrible. The worst thing was that I knew Tom had a child back home (Tom came from another country); I had always known about the boy but it hadn't really mattered. Tom had always sent money when he could and kept in touch with the child's mother,

133

> *but he had not seen his son since he was a baby. That was the agreement with the mother, who had other children. After we lost Alicia and then I couldn't get pregnant again I felt we were both being punished. Tom didn't want to say anything to the doctor or the clinic so he went through those sperm tests, when we knew it must be me who was the problem. He was good at first, very laid back about it really, I suppose he had proved he was fertile; it was me who was the failure. After IVF failed the second time Tom began to feel that we shouldn't go on. He might have had all the right reasons but I couldn't see past the little boy he already had. We couldn't talk about it because it just turned into rows and eventually we split up. We did talk to the counsellor but I felt they were assuming that we were both the same and it stopped me saying anything. They also never mentioned that Tom was black or asked about our families and that seemed a bit funny, like they were not able or willing to deal with us as people. I desperately needed to talk but it seemed too hard in the short time we had, it seemed to be just about getting pregnant and that wasn't the only issue.'*

Single women and lesbian women also felt that they were not always given the same regard as couples. 'I felt they were tiptoeing around the issues, I didn't want to be treated as a freak but the fact that I was a lesbian had to be acknowledged. I'm not ashamed of it and when it is not acknowledged I feel they are uncomfortable with it. It took some courage to go to the clinic and a great deal of thought between me and my partner and I suppose I wanted that understood.'

Some couples also felt that the clinic was not geared up to deal with them together. 'They had to muster a spare chair from a cubby-hole, they didn't seem to be expecting us both.'

Most of all they wanted their fears and feelings validated. They did not want to be told that it was all OK and they would 'be sorted out'. They wanted to feel that their particular situation was being regarded in a non-judgemental and supportive way.

Treatment

Many clients felt that starting treatment was a positive but frightening experience. They felt that they had to give it their best and be committed to it, partly in order to make it work. They wanted to feel that the whole team supported them in this. There was belief, hope and expectation. Alongside this there was an awareness of the loss of control and privacy, the need to hand over something very personal and private to the professionals. Some found this difficult with a sense of 'just being a set of case notes'; indeed, one woman felt that she did not just want the clinic 'to think about us while we're there, I want them to be spending time thinking about our situation'. This need to remain a real person to the people who were treating them was very strongly expressed.

Again the need for clear explanations of the treatment, its processes, procedures and side-effects was stressed by the clients. They wanted to feel they were being given honest and complete answers. One woman said that 'I have been shattered by being given wrong information. I can handle disappointment and bad news but I have found it very difficult to deal with hopes that have proved false. Through this my trust . . . has been significantly undermined'. Most felt that their medical care had been good but that their emotional needs were overlooked or only paid lip service to. This was particularly so in the time between treatments. 'As soon as they've replaced the embryos, that's it. Up to that there are scheduled appointments and after that it's nothing. You know you have just failed, you ask them if everything is OK and they just say "I'm sorry". They put the phone down and that's the end of it, I think you need to talk to somebody.'

The difficulties that treatment raised for the couple were mainly two-fold. In one case the male partner said that he felt he was 'seen as a sperm provider, not a participant in procreation'. Some felt that although they may have seen infertility as a problem for them as a couple, when it came to treatment it was the woman who became the focus of attention and the needs of the man were not regarded as important. Clients also expressed anxiety about how both their lives were affected in every area by the decision to have treatment. Some felt that 'life has been put on hold, I don't go for promotion at work, I don't plan holidays anymore, we always seem to be waiting'. Some felt they were always asking for something; time off work, prescriptions from the GP, care for other children and in some cases financial help from family or friends.

A major area of difficulty for the couple is the decision whether or not to pursue treatment. How the decision to stop treatment is taken is a real problem. Some felt that the clinic should decide, and that decision may be made on the grounds of policy, a certain number of cycles only being available or on medical grounds. Some felt that they were 'pulled through the system; there never seemed to be a time when we could honestly talk to each other about going on'. Good counselling was very much appreciated in this area of decision-making. Some clients felt that they had been given the time and space to think through all the options, to be honest with each other and to look at their realistic expectations of becoming parents. Some counsellors were able to allow the partners to have different reactions to the decision and to have the opportunity to be sad and express their pain. This was particularly expressed in relation to considering changes to treatment such as using donor sperm, eggs or embryos, or the possibility of surrogacy. They felt the implications of this were profound, particularly for the partner who would not be the genetic parent, but also for their future as a couple and as parents.

In many of the replies from clients the need for trained counsellors was emphasized. Many were full of praise for the help and support they had received and felt that it had been professional and compassionate. However, some of them had experienced clumsy if well-meaning help that had been more upsetting. One woman who had experienced several miscarriages was told that 'if it causes you so much pain, stop trying'. Good counselling had opened up issues that they felt diffident about opening for themselves, fearing the distress it might cause the partner. Many felt that access to a counsellor throughout the period of diagnosis and treatment was important. They did not feel that they necessarily required 'therapy' but more the opportunity to be heard and attended to, to have someone who could suggest the questions it was difficult to ask and who would support you whatever your decision and whatever your reaction. When treatment does not succeed it reawakens all their feelings of personal failure and added to this is the sense of letting down the clinic, 'Everyone is saying I'm sorry'.

Ending treatment

For almost every person embarking on the process of fertility treatment, being pregnant has been the goal. Once they are pregnant or have recognized that they want to stop trying to be pregnant, there has to be a re-focusing.

BEING PREGNANT

Alongside the usual doubts, fears and excitement felt when pregnant, those who have reached their goal by assisted conception have some very different feelings. They have been treated as special for some time and now may be handed over to the care of an antenatal clinic that will treat them like any other consumer of the service. One woman pregnant for the first time by IVF said that she felt 'abandoned by the clinic; I was just anyone at antenatal clinic and it was only when there was a problem and I was admitted at 30 weeks did I feel they were regarding the pregnancy as special. The thing that most mothers dread became reassuring to me, this institutionalization really worried me later on'.

Some clients have so lost confidence in their body and its ability to support the pregnancy that they have little concept of what is normal in pregnancy and fear they are over- or under-reacting to changes.

A few clients expressed anxiety about whether to tell staff in the antenatal and delivery wards about their assisted conception. Some felt that this was the first time they had to make this decision and would have liked help before deciding what they should say. This was particularly true of those who had assisted conception using a donor or who were surrogate parents. One woman expressed her difficulty in talking to her partner about another pregnancy. She did not feel that one child was a family for her, yet was aware that her partner had said he 'never wanted to go through all that again'. She felt that she needed someone with whom to discuss this after the birth of her child and at a time when she felt ready to consider another pregnancy. When she mentioned it to her family they felt she should be happy with what she had and she felt too distanced from the clinic to ask them. She thought that this area should have been addressed during the previous pregnancy.

NOT BEING A PARENT

Some clients felt that they wanted to have this acknowledged as a decision, not just assumed to be a failure. They needed help to find how to talk about it and help with how to explain their feelings. They also needed space to feel sad and bad, and help to regain their lives. Some felt they should have been warned of the feelings of loss and bereavement that they experienced and how to share that with their partner. They needed 'someone to be with you, to look at what your feelings are and your thoughts for the future; you can't go on for ever trying to be a parent'.

At all stages of the process of asking for help with conception, clients felt they needed care and empathy. They needed clear information, help with understanding the choices open to them, and time and space to explore their feelings. They wanted their individuality accepted and their feelings validated.

Chapter 7

Counselling for the Experience of Infertility

Access to counselling at the beginning of infertility is limited and yet it is the time when couples felt they wanted space to be able to talk about what seeking help might mean for them. Some GP surgeries do have counsellors attached to the surgery but the GP may not recognize the need for counselling at this stage, regarding it as a medical problem. This highlights the difficulty in dealing with infertility: on one hand there are clear medical reasons why people have trouble getting pregnant and on the other hand medicalizing the issue tends to take away focus from the deep feelings raised by not conceiving. Those who waited longer than a year to seek help and those who spent years with their GP or a local gynaecologist who was not a specialist in infertility, without any clear diagnosis or treatment, felt quite angry about the delay.

> *Mandy and Colin had decided to start planning their family in their twenties. Mandy felt quite clearly that 'having to wait for over a year or so is too long for you, even though medically speaking you are still quite young. The tests drag on over such a long time, and they say have this test done and in a couple of months we will*

do another one and on and on. The consultant gynaecologist seemed to think something will happen in the meantime so don't worry about it'. Something did happen to them in fact: two spontaneous conceptions and miscarriages. They felt they were then 'left to drift' without any clear indication of what they could expect in the future. Colin felt 'most vulnerable' during the first couple of years of investigation and treatment. He would have liked to have had the opportunity of counselling which he felt would help him during this new experience to understand his feelings and enable him to decide what to do next. He also said 'if there is counselling when you get to IVF that's useful I suppose for the stress you will go through with IVF, but by that time you should have, possibly most people will have come to some understanding of their situation and not require it quite so much generally, only in relation to the strain of IVF'.

Clear information concerning reasons for infertility, investigations and treatment options may not be given by the GP when they are first approached as they may assume it is unlikely to be a major problem. Many couples were told 'not to worry, go home and try a bit longer'. The couple, however, wish to have the whole picture to give them some control over what lies ahead, to make plans and decisions.

There are no data for the number of people who do not pursue further investigations or treatments, but we suggest there could be many who feel unable to approach anyone for help. Having literature about infertility available at all points of healthcare would enable those who find it difficult to ask to have access to information they need about local services. The role of Family Planning Clinics is valuable as they have a different accent on the care they offer. Being concerned with fertility they are aware of the emotional needs of the individual and the significance of the impact of conception. Some clinics do offer initial information, and in some cases testing, before referral to a fertility clinic.

WHAT CAN COUNSELLING OFFER

It was clear from the replies to our questionnaires and from talking to couples, that telling any professional about their infertility actually made real a problem they had been experiencing for some considerable time. It was not a new issue for them; however, it was a new issue for the GP and couples wanted recognition, as well as the medical attention, that changes were already happening in their lives.

Counselling can offer acknowledgement that there is a problem and that a solution will be sought. This problem greatly affects all parts of their lives. Some felt that it directed who they could spend time with, both at work and in their social lives. Peers who plan their lives around pregnancy and children are sometimes too painful to be with. Parents who make clear their wishes for grandchildren also raise uncomfortable feelings. Both men and women may have been paying serious attention to taking care of their bodies in preparation for becoming parents, changing diets, daily habits and carefully timing intercourse for 'the right time in the month'. All of these lifestyle changes need to be acknowledged and validated. At this time there is also the disappointment of not conceiving and some may need to talk about the personal issues this raises.

Sometimes permission is needed to express thoughts and doubts about the experience so far and also about where to go from here. In a couple relationship each individual in counselling may be given permission to express their different reactions and to talk more freely between themselves – to share rather than withhold. There can be a fear that expressing pain will wound or damage the other and possibly the relationship. Counselling can offer space and time to express these feelings. Indeed it may be the only safe space to express anger, frustration, guilt and fear because there is a fantasy that negative feelings lead to negative outcomes.

As already highlighted, initially the counsellor may need to offer information about outcomes of investigations and options for treatment. This requires a working knowledge of the causes and treatment of infertility and information about local treatment centres. Those who had been offered this early felt much more in control of their situation and more able to return to their GP for support after they had been referred to a clinic.

The theme of support may continue for some time through investigations and may re-occur through lengthy unsuccessful treatments. If it was possible to have access to a counsellor at the beginning, individuals could establish a basis for contact that could be of benefit to them individually or as a couple as a one-off session at a time of decision or crisis, or short- or long-term work in a therapeutic alliance.

> *Lynn and Paul had established a good relationship with their GP so that telling her of the problems they were experiencing getting pregnant was easy. Lynn said 'I have always felt able to talk with her about anything. After our investigations and my laparoscopy, she was the first person to mention IVF to me even though all of our tests were normal. She referred me to the clinic and always kept a keen interest in my treatment. I just knew that if there was a problem she would be there to listen to me even though she is a busy person. Sometimes she let me cry when I felt bad, which was quite often, and she never told me to be brave or look on the bright side or any of those platitudes. She just had to be the first person I wanted to tell when we got pregnant'.*

Therapeutic counselling at this stage will only be appropriate for a few who recognize emerging issues that require attention before progressing further. The Human Fertilization and Embroyology Authority Code of Practice (1995) views counselling as something 'people should be able to seek at any stage in their *investigations* and treatments'. In practice, counselling is rarely available without charge before referral to a licensed clinic. At the clinics it is required to be offered as part of the offer of treatment. The issue of independent therapeutic counselling that may be long term can be dealt with by a clinic by referring outside the unit for which a cost may be incurred. Counsellors employed by a clinic may not have the time to commit to long-term therapy so energies can be concentrated on short-term focused work. Counsellors need to be aware that they will be picking up all the issues that have been left unaddressed through the investigative period.

Counselling needs may be varied depending on the issues raised for the individual. Those in same sex and non-sexual relationships may be seeking help to have a baby without any medical cause. They are fearful of the reaction they will encounter and anxious about letting go. Clinics do not state clearly if they are willing to treat those not in a heterosexual relationship and they may feel judgements are already be being made about their need for treatment. Within the counselling framework they may have the opportunity to acknowledge their personal choice in a space where they won't be judged. Here they can prepare for the as yet unknown demands of the system, examine their history if they choose, and explore areas of personal concern.

WHO CAN COUNSEL?

In relation to the expressed needs of clients for acknowledgement permission and information, who can offer the opportunity to explore these issues? Anyone who can offer time, space and the basic counselling skills of listening, attending, empathy and genuineness will be the right person. It may be the GP, practice nurse, family planning clinic doctor or nurse; indeed, few others will be involved at the beginning of recognition of a problem and the early investigative period. Assessment of therapeutic needs requires those who offer counselling to have knowledge of when it would be appropriate to refer and what is available through other relevant agencies and their areas of expertise.

Many couples talked of the important role played by the national support groups at this point. They were a source of help when no-one else listened. Through their helplines couples heard of others experiencing the same issues and the recognition of shared experiences came as a great relief. For some it ended feelings of isolation and enabled them to seek out local groups where they could meet and talk about issues important to them. Some preferred the anonymity of the newsletter but gained strength from just knowing someone out there knew what it was like.

George put off seeing his GP even though Natalie had pleaded with him to go with her. It began to affect their relationship seriously but he just couldn't face the ordeal. 'I felt he would be making all sorts of judgements about me and my manhood. I was also petrified that it could be my fault, my problem. Whilst I put off seeing him I could put off facing any of these problems.' Natalie felt she couldn't go behind George's back and go to the GP herself but after reading an article on infertility in a magazine she contacted Child and received their newsletter. George picked up the newsletter one day and reading through he recognized that others had the same anxieties and fears. 'It was such a relief to see how others had dealt with the same sort of feelings I was grappling with. I also realised what refusing to go and see the GP was doing to Natalie and our marriage.'

It is evident that information about infertility, its causes and treatments is required so that insight can be gained about the commitment about to be undertaken. Factual information available from Issue and Child helped some to work through the processes involved in the medical aspects of infertility. This was especially pertinent for those who wanted to feel some degree of control.

INVESTIGATIONS

The range of tests and investigations that now need to be completed before a diagnosis can be made focus around the woman. In many cases it is the woman who visits her GP and her partner may only be asked to give a sperm sample for analysis. If the couple are not seen together at this stage it is possible for the man to start to feel less valued as a full partner in the proceedings. Tests may be started by the GP, with referral to a gynaecology clinic or infertility clinic coming later, or the GP may refer directly to a specialist clinic depending on the wishes of the couple, the expertise of the GP, the knowledge of an ongoing medical condition and the availability of a specialist opinion.

This is an active phase, and much attention is being paid to the problem with the hope that these investigations will bring the solution. Issues about not conceiving are put on hold. Many people talked of delays encountered when tests needed to be repeated or results were lost. There did seem to be disparity over the length of time it took to complete the basic tests, which correlated well with the degree of frustration and anger experienced.

What Can Counselling Offer?

Couples did not seem to feel much of a need for talking about their problem through this part of their experience of infertility. They wanted to remain positive and hopeful about the outcome. However, there was space to look at the differences between the experiences of the man and the woman. At this point their roles had changed, the woman becoming 'the patient' and the man taking on a more supportive and caring role. Many men told us that they felt confused and left out and they wanted acknowledgement that they had an important part to play. They felt they were expected to remain distanced from the problem as the medical team continued to concentrate on their partners. The counsellor needs to be able to pay attention to the different needs of the man, to 'hold' him and allow his feelings to be expressed. As already alluded to in George's story, there may be real anxieties about blame and guilt arising from worrying about the results of semen analysis.

Information about the investigations helps the woman to make sense of what is happening to her. The counsellor will need to be aware that while concentration is on the outcome of these investigations it may not be possible to achieve much in a therapeutic alliance. However, it is important to be available and recognize that there may be difficulties experienced in undergoing such invasive procedures as post-coital tests and laparoscopy with no pregnancy at the end.

DIAGNOSIS

Diagnostic procedures may in themselves result in a pregnancy. When they do not then all hope in the fantasy that it could happen is lost. Remaining childless is once again a reality. Couples remembered clearly how they were told this information and of being left alone to deal with the news and face each other. Some called it a life sentence, which eloquently expresses the depth of emotion stirred up for both men and women. For the majority, counselling was not on offer at this stage and yet it is here that life-changing decisions are made: whether to go for treatment, stop or pursue other possibilities such as adoption.

All the positive and hopeful feelings give way at this point to a range of negative feelings. Shock, anger, blame, guilt, loss, sense of failure and deep sadness are all words used to describe the feelings experienced and for many there was no space to take these issues and so they remained isolated, not knowing what to do or where to go. It is at the time of diagnosis that counselling would be of most benefit.

What the Counsellor Can Do

Counsellors can offer to give attention to these bad feelings. It is important to establish a place of safety where judgements will not be made about negative reactions. Individuals may project their anger onto GPs or medical or nursing staff in an effort to remain the 'good patient'. In the counselling alliance the counsellor can offer a space where they don't have to be good and don't have to apologise for being bad.

The counsellor may be needed to offer confirmation that it is unlikely that a pregnancy will occur without medical help. This can be confusing, especially for those for whom there is only the negative diagnosis of 'unexplained infertility'.

The counsellor has to be aware of the need to stay with the client and the pain. It is being there that is important to the client so that they can recognize that it is bearable and others can bear to be with them through this awful time. The helping professions of medicine and nursing are experienced in assisting in a solving process and so may experience a need to 'make things better' in what they see as a helping process. It is important to be aware that this is where they are required to adopt a counselling stance and not attempt to do something or give false reassurance. In suggesting a particular treatment a client may avoid working through his/her painful feelings about the situation and follow a treatment because of that suggestion with painful personal consequences.

Rahid and Jamal had kept secret the fact that they were having treatment with donor sperm. They had chosen a clinic far away from them recommended by their GP. They had quickly pursued donor insemination after discovering Jamal had a really low sperm count and were doubtful about undergoing IVF treatment with ICSI because it was still a very new procedure. Rahid said, 'We didn't really talk about it, we just agreed that we would go ahead with the simplest treatment available to get our baby. When the first attempt failed I was shocked but we could go again and then I got pregnant. At first it was OK and I was happy but as time went on I began to think about what was growing inside me and where it had come from. I began to wonder about the donor: who was he?, why had he donated his sperm? and how will it affect my baby?'. Rahid came to counselling to talk these issues through during her pregnancy. She had spent weeks feeling confused, frightened and in tears unable to talk with anyone, especially her partner. No-one could understand why she was acting so strangely and in fact someone had suggested that if she didn't want to be pregnant

she could have a termination. She felt quite
angry that neither her doctor nor the clinic had
suggested that they take time out to consider
options and implications before embarking on
treatment.

Rahid had not had the opportunity to think about the
implications of carrying a baby from an unknown man.
Counselling should now be offered to all for whom donor eggs,
sperm or embryos is the proposed treatment and if it has not
been offered before, then at this stage of the infertility process
counselling should be considered a normal step in the
psychological progress through infertility. Couples often said
that if they were offered counselling they felt it had to do with
people going mad and felt quite anxious about it. Those who did
go, for the most part, found the experience helpful. Much
depends on how the counselling is introduced by the clinicians
and the value counselling is seen to have throughout the whole
process.

MAKING DECISIONS

After the shock of diagnosis comes the difficult area of making
decisions. Some couples had clear visions of what to do next and
felt able to take control over what to do. They may have been
working through some of this already because they were aware
of the impact of medical complications on fertility. When
diagnosis was not a shock but a confirmation of a suspected
problem then there was a sense of relief that at last this was
acknowledged and now they could move on.

By now some couples felt caught up in a process that was
difficult to stop. They had doubts about what going on would
mean for them but they had no place to express these feelings
either to themselves or each other. It was as if they wanted some
space to review what had been happening. Only then could they
make the decision that was right for them. Women often
expressed a need to talk with their partners about their feelings.
This sometimes becomes a no-go area through the stress of all the

investigations and, as already highlighted, men who were feeling less then full partners in this experience found it difficult suddenly to be brought on board again when their agreement on further action was required.

> *Carol and Mike had one 6-year-old daughter who was conceived without any problem. Carol became anxious when after a couple of years of trying there was no pregnancy. Mike, however, was prepared to wait, so another year passed before they were referred to the infertility clinic. Carol recalled, 'I went alone because Mike couldn't get the time off work and then it just seemed to carry on like that. Each visit seemed to bring more tests for me and Mike's sperm count was fine so there didn't seem to be much to worry about there'. Eventually when the investigations were complete they were told they could only offer a diagnosis of unexplained infertility for which the clinic would recommend trying parenteral induction of ovulation. Mike says, 'At this point I was feeling quite alone, Carol kept going on about her need to have a baby and I guess I felt there was no space for me. I didn't want to start treatment whilst I was feeling this way so it came as quite a shock to her when I wouldn't agree to take part. I sure got her attention though and we spent some time with a counsellor working through our different feelings. I'm glad we did because I realized how much I wanted another child. I just felt I had to decide that for myself'.*

What the Counsellor Can Do

Counselling can enable the decision-making process to be started by reflecting back what the client is bringing to the session. Some couples wanted to talk through with someone other than the doctor just what going on to treatment would mean for them. They acknowledged that this was an important part of helping them to deal with the stresses involved in accepting treatment. Having found this space they felt more able to ask for it again when treatment failed. They also felt more able to use the safety of a counselling session to share with each other thoughts and feelings they feared may hurt their partner and to recognize their differing individual needs. The client needs to move on from the passive experience of having things done to the active phase of taking some control. Neither the client nor the counsellor may be aware of what that decision may be. In order to facilitate this process the counsellor will require some understanding of the options available. These will range from possible infertility treatments (including the use of donor gametes and surrogacy) and adoption (both inland and overseas) to the choice to stop at this point and remain childless.

TREATMENT

Starting Treatment

This is the time when the couple are most caught up in the medical procedures and most want to remain positive and hopeful. There is less attention paid by them to their feelings at this time and they seem to expect this to be mirrored by the clinic staff. It is a time for concentrating on the body and almost giving the emotions a rest. Many do not want to be involved with counselling then.

The counsellor can be most helpful in an encouraging and supportive role. Their knowledge of the process of treatment will be useful to the client and the ongoing contact will enable them to use counselling as they move on to further treatment, pregnancy or the decisions about a family by other means.

Continuing Treatment

However much the infertile recognize cognitively that treatment is not always successful, the failure to conceive is always distressing, bringing with it feelings of failure, anger, guilt and hopelessness. Yet so much is built on hope, on continuing to hope that they will have a child, hoping that the clinic will be able to help and hoping that next time it will be right. The lack of hope is also seen as a reason for not being pregnant. Part of the 'baby magic' is that you have to remain positive for it to work. Thus the myth continues that the couple, or at least the woman, must remain hopeful because if any doubts are expressed they will be translated into failure. Good thoughts are powerful, but hard to maintain in the face of failure.

Not conceiving after treatment places the couple in the position not just of facing what feels like personal failure but also the decision about whether to try again and the implications of this for their state of mind, financial position and their day-to-day life. They will possibly be offered the chance to try again in a few months time. They then have to decide whether they want to do this. Most find the decision to stop very hard. They have often spent years of their life together planning to have a family and suffering the monthly reminder of failure. They may have been positively focused on success and prepared to devote a great deal of their life and sometimes money to achieving this. Deciding to stop means making a change in their plans, their hopes and their thinking. Even having to wait for another treatment cycle implies having to let go of the hope and anticipation for a little while. Many couples spoke to us of putting 'life on hold' whilst they went through treatment. They did not want to make any changes 'just in case' a pregnancy meant that these changes became irrelevant. Many chose not to go on holiday or to move house. They needed the money to be available for treatment or they needed to stay within reach of the clinic. Several women said that they had not wanted to change their jobs during this time. They were aware of feeling that going for promotion might be an acknowledgement that they were not going to be a mother. Some were uncertain about whether a different employer would allow them time off for treatment or that new colleagues would 'ask too many questions'. For many, their childlessness was no longer remarkable where they worked but a new job put them in the position of having to explain.

Anna is 40 years old and has two children aged 10 and 9. She was divorced 6 years ago and remarried last year. Because of her age they decided to try to conceive immediately, but when this did not happen after 6 months, Anna decided to seek help. 'I became very concerned about it early on. I had no trouble before and had not thought there would be a problem. There seemed to be so much invested in a pregnancy. I don't think David was actually as worried about it as I was. It became for me a condition of the success of the relationship that I became pregnant. I was more depressed with every sign of failure. My period arriving threw me for days. I didn't want to work or look after the girls or anything. I began to feel that if I was unable to do something so simple, how could I do anything well? I kept buying pregnancy test kits and checking the mucus. I couldn't pass a magazine rack without looking for articles about infertility and I ordered and read every book in the library. It began to feel like a secret vice! I suppose I became obsessed. The GP was good and responded to my demands for urgent treatment. The clinic did offer counselling and the nurse who did this was well informed about the treatment but I felt that I had to keep being positive. They all smiled and seemed to think everything was going to be all right, so I felt I had to be the same. David always came with me and was very supportive, but after the first treatment failed, I felt I needed something for me. I needed to protect him from my feelings of despair and anger. I eventually asked to be referred to a counsellor outside the clinic on my own. She did not know much about fertility but I could talk about feelings with her. Then I was cross with her for not knowing enough and stopped going.'

What the Counsellor can do

Anna and many of the other women and couples we talked to were asking for support, information and understanding of their feelings, hopes, fears and doubts, just as they were at every stage. The failure of their first treatment had left them feeling uncertain, angry or sad, however much they and the staff had tried to prepare them.

The counsellor must be able to offer to 'hold' the client through this difficult time. The client is having to cope with failure and also believe in success, to decide whether to try to fulfil their dreams or to abandon them and change their life goals. Many of the patients we spoke to felt that it was crucial that the counsellor had the medical information so that they would not have to explain the situation. When this was not available it caused irritation and was felt to be a waste of time. Some felt that it made the counsellor seem remote and they began to doubt whether they would be able to understand other issues. Nor did they want to feel that the counsellor was trying to move them on too quickly. They wanted some information about other possibilities if they were to decide not to continue but many said that at this stage they still needed to feel that it could have a positive outcome and so talk of adoption or fostering felt like giving up.

The counsellor has the opportunity to help the couple to move from the disappointment of not conceiving to deciding where they want to go in the future, whether they want to continue treatment, to change the treatment or to consider alternative life goals.

The counsellor has to form a relationship with a couple often at a time of crisis, when they may have experienced difficulty conceiving for some time and be at the point of making life-changing decisions. They may be experiencing feelings of loss and grieving and may be unsure of their relationship and the effects of infertility on the relationship. The counsellor does not always know whether the work will be a one-off session, short-term focused counselling or longer-term therapy. The principles of establishing the relationship between counsellor and client are the same and the ethics and boundaries of the counselling are not affected.

153

Burnard (1989) identifies eight stages in the progress of the counselling relationship that may be useful in looking at the way the counsellor may work in infertility.

- stage 1: meeting the client
- stage 2: discussion of surface issues
- stage 3: revelation of deeper issues
- stage 4: ownership of feelings and emotional release
- stage 5: generation of insight
- stage 6: problem solving, future planning
- stage 7: action by the client
- stage 8: disengagement from the counselling relationship by the client.

Stage 1 involves the counsellor making the clients feel at ease and encouraging them to look at their reasons for seeking counselling or how counselling may be able to help. This is particularly true in infertility where they may never have considered counselling or may be rather suspicious of it.

The second stage is the client beginning to tell the story. There is no expectation of deep levels of self-disclosure, these are experienced in the next stage. The client now feels safe with the counsellor and confident that they are to be trusted with the 'less good' parts of themselves. These may be at the level of 'I don't know how much longer I can go on with treatment. I feel so sad every time it fails'. Stage 3 is the expression of feelings at a deeper level. This may bring in feelings not just about the loss of fertility but other issues about their relationships or history.

The fourth stage is the ownership of feelings. The client is now able to accept that they have bad feelings and to express them. Cheryl was eventually able to say 'I feel so angry about not being able to have a child; I feel envious of other people and don't even want to spend time with them. When a friend had a baby recently I couldn't send a card; I don't want to see her and I definitely don't want to see the baby'. This was followed by the release of feelings through angry tears that she had not allowed herself before, feeling that she had to 'be good' and keep positive to help herself and others. The counsellor needs to allow the expression of these feelings for this stage to be helpful. Insight comes in the next phase, stage 5, when the client begins to see more clearly. This may be the result of the expression of pent-up feelings, and the connection of these feelings with present action or past experiences. Stage 6 is problem-solving. The release of feelings and seeing the situation more clearly may not be enough and the client may want to consider where they go from there. Burnard suggests a problem-solving cycle that moves the client from *problem identification*, clearly defining the problem, to *generation of possible solutions* brainstorming all possible avenues and rejecting nothing, to *prioritization*, when the client sets the shortlist of options. This is followed by the *choice of solution* in which the client plans its implementation and moves on to the final stage of *action*. If after it is applied it does not work, then the client returns to stage 1 of the process.

The client will not necessarily progress through these stages in order nor need the same length of time in each stage, but it may be a useful guide for the counsellor as to a client's progress or where they might be 'stuck' and spending a lot of time. Another map of counselling is the three-stage model developed by Egan (1982) (see Chapter 4).

We would like to suggest another model that may be appropriate when working with infertile clients, when the counsellor may need to do intensive, short-term focused work. This looks at four stages of the client's needs. Again, these may not take the same length of time or need the same amount of attention. This will depend on the client's state of mind, needs and past experiences. The four areas of need are:

- holding: helping the clients to deal with the initial feelings of loss, disappointment and failure
- cognition: understanding their feelings and sharing these with their partner if appropriate
- coping: identifying helpful coping mechanisms and helping the client to implement them
- deciding: making plans for the future.

Holding

The concept of *'holding'* is a very important one for clients who are between treatments or having to make the decision to continue. It means the ability to be 'with' a client, not pushing for change, not trying to change their state of mind in a positive way but allowing the client the time and space to look at their feelings. It means being very aware of not having your own agenda but responding to that of the client. It may mean being able to be with their pain and fear and not trying to make it better. Empty reassurance will be unusable by the client. 'There's nothing to worry about' never made anyone stop worrying. It just makes them feel that someone else does not feel that they are justified in worrying. It is part of holding that the client does not have the extra pressure of trying to please the counsellor. If the client feels that he cannot tolerate their pain or wants to minimize it, the client may try to protect the counsellor and therefore not express the true extent of the feelings. Equally, if clients are not encouraged to feel validated in their feelings they will wonder if they should be feeling this way. Acceptance that the feelings are normal is a major part of the help that can be offered to clients. Many people who had joined support groups felt that this was their greatest benefit.

Holding can be hard on the counsellor. It is never easy to be alongside people who are suffering and for whom we are unable to do anything that seems a positive help. It may be particularly hard for those who come to counselling from the other helping professions, where there is an emphasis on 'doing something to make things better' and where not making it better may be seen as a shortcoming of the professional.

Cognition

Once the client has been allowed to experience the bad feelings they may be able to move on to understanding some of them. When we feel distressed or depressed it is often difficult to identify just what we are experiencing. We feel overwhelmed with bad feelings without really knowing what those feelings are. We may also be uncomfortable at recognizing them. Our society does not happily sanction the expression of anger, fear and sadness. There still remains a need to maintain a stiff upper lip, especially for men. In not wanting to have the feeling we often fail to identify it – we just feel bad. Helping the couple to 'name' the feelings can often help them to seem less overwhelming. It also helps them to talk to each other and to 'rehearse' talking to others. Saying things in front of the counsellor may feel safer than saying them directly to a partner or the family. The assumption that the counsellor can cope with them, particularly if they have been there in the holding phase, and can act as interpreter, if necessary helps the client to feel secure. Anger, fear, guilt and shame can be hard to admit to; if the counsellor can accept these feelings in a non-judgemental way it can help to normalize them for the client. They can be more safely expressed to, and shared with, others. Once they are out in the open they often do not feel as bad and the client may be able to move on from carrying the burden of bad feelings.

Recognizing and understanding feelings requires us as counsellors to be very aware of the client's needs and to help them become aware. It was only as she talked to the counsellor that Anna realized she was becoming obsessed with being pregnant and that her whole life was affected by it. She had not recognized the extent to which she had abandoned the rest of her life. Her counsellor allowed these feelings to emerge as she talked to Anna about how she felt and what she wanted for the future. It was Anna who was able to make the connections. Some clients need more help to explore feelings and the counsellor may have to ask more questions and make some of the connections between thought and behaviour, always checking back with the client that the counsellor is not making false assumptions. Allowing feelings of anger or fear to be present helps the client to explore them. If the counsellor is in a position to offer longer-term counselling they may also begin to look at the client's past experiences of failure and to examine how they felt then. We all carry our past experiences with us and if our present pain has echoes in the past these feelings can be brought back, so that we are not just dealing with our feelings now but also those that belong in the past and perhaps have never really been dealt with. There are various techniques that may help the client identify these areas, some of which have been discussed in Chapter 4. Some clients are able to use art or drama therapy to express non-verbally how they feel. This need not be as frightening as clients fear and they may find that drawing or painting their feelings with support from a therapist brings not only recognition and insight but also release. Equally, drama therapy can offer a safe way of exploring and releasing feelings. For those who can verbalize the feelings they may be able to use a 'two-chair' technique as used in Gestalt therapy, where the client is encouraged to talk to a 'person' in the empty chair to say what they would like them to hear but cannot say in reality. However, none of these techniques should be used by counsellors who are not trained in them.

Several of the couples we talked to felt that they wanted to be involved in longer-term counselling, recognizing that their infertility had exposed other unresolved issues. Where this was not offered, and they found it difficult either to ask for or to find it, there was a real feeling of abandonment. Their needs were not being met, and they sometimes became angry with each other or the clinic.

Coping

Coping is not about ignoring or minimizing the problem; so many people feel that to be seen to be coping, they must give the impression that they are dealing with everything as normal. Coping is about being able to look at emotions and begin to explore how those feelings fit into their experience. However, there may be a time when the couple or individual feel that they want to take some control of how they feel and act. Helping the infertile couple or individual to explore their coping mechanisms is an important part of helping them to move on. They need to understand that they can go on with their lives, that they can take some control and deal with the feelings. Advice-giving at this stage may be counter-therapeutic and is rarely helpful. Information may be sought and offered but advice takes control away from the client, when they need encouragement to look at their own coping resources. It also sets up the counsellor as an expert. This may encourage the rather childlike feeling of anyone subjected to medical procedures and make the client dependent on the counsellor.

One way to help clients to look at their coping mechanisms is to examine how they have coped in the past. At a time of crisis it is easy to feel that we have never been able to cope or will be able to again. It sometimes helps to look at past coping strategies. Do they feel better if they cry, if they take themselves out of the situation to a new place; do they need to talk about the problem as much as possible? Every individual has a different way of dealing with distress and they may need help to recognize this and to accept that their partner, friends and family may all have their own way. Validation of their feelings and needs makes this process easier. They also can be helped to realize that coping mechanisms are not fixed; they can be adapted and changed where they have proved to be ineffective.

Decision-making

The infertile couple or woman may be faced with constant decision-making during the process of assisted conception. When she has had an unsuccessful treatment and is given the option to continue, the decision-making takes on enormous significance. She must choose to continue to try in the face of failure that may be unexplained and inexplicable.

We make decisions based on facts, feelings and fantasies. When they are looking at the facts the client wants to know what went wrong and whether it could go wrong again. They need to know about the alternatives and the choices they may have to face. Here the well informed counsellor can be very supportive. The client needs clear information when they can accept it and in a form that they can understand. This may mean that written information can be helpful; this can be taken away and read when they are ready, shared and discussed. If they then have access to someone to whom they can address questions, they may again feel ready to take control and make a decision.

Most of us also make decisions based on our feelings; when it is clear what the sensible course of action should be it is amazing how many people do not pursue it! We act from fear, anger, love and the pursuit of our dreams. Being able to talk about these with a counsellor and have them accepted and not judged may help the client to understand the basis of their decision and feel more able to 'own' it. We also act on our fantasies – for many infertile women there is always the wanted child present. To decide to stop trying to reach this child may seem like a betrayal. The resulting feelings of loss and grief may feel overwhelming.

Some patients will be in the position of having to make the next decision of whether to accept their childlessness or to consider adoption or fostering. To make this choice when still dealing with feelings of loss and grieving is expecting a lot of anyone and it may be that this period of grieving needs time before further decisions are made. If the couple decide to adopt there will be assessments and support from the social worker, but this may in itself feel difficult to face at this time. The counsellor may need to help the couple to give themselves the space they need.

Support for Other Staff

The counsellor may be in a position to support other members of staff. It is not just the clients who experience the disappointment of failure. Staff also want to 'succeed' and produce the perfect baby, and they share the need to remain positive and hopeful. Everyone who works with infertile patients is aware that sometimes there will be no baby; however, they continue to strive to help the couple. If this help is only seen in terms of a baby then they will experience failure. When it can be seen as enabling the couple or woman to have the best chance of a child then they can be satisfied that they tried. Members of staff also share the client's need to protect other people from bad feelings and may feel anxious about expressing their own. Staff also carry their own needs and feelings and these may sometimes enhance and occasionally intrude on the work that they do. The counsellor, who should be supervised and trained to take regard of his or her own feelings, may be able to help others to pay attention to this.

COUNSELLING FOR THE OUTCOME OF TREATMENT

There are two possible outcomes of treatment, both of which may benefit from counselling support. The woman may become pregnant or the couple or the clinic may decide to stop treatment. This decision to stop may come near the beginning or after a long commitment to trying to have a baby. The couple will have to face the future without a child to whom they have given birth and also decide whether they intend to pursue adoption or surrogacy.

160

Becoming Pregnant

When pregnancy becomes a reality instead of a fantasy, some women are surprised that they feel uncertain and fearful or that tensions arise in the relationship that were not there during years of infertility treatment. Pregnancy is a stressful as well as a joyful time for many women; they are faced with not just a change in their bodies but in their whole lives. They know that nothing is ever going to be quite the same again. If people who have had problems becoming pregnant have avoided pregnant friends, or family or others have striven to protect them, they may not be aware of the normality of many of these feelings. It may also feel like a betrayal of the baby to express any doubts or fears about it. Some women have expressed feelings that they were more interested in the pregnancy once it was a reality than their partners, when they had seemed so supportive during treatment. The long-term effect of low self-esteem for those who have had problems conceiving may remain during the pregnancy, when they may doubt whether they can be adequate parents.

For those who have been involved in support groups there may even be feelings of guilt at being the one who is pregnant when others are still trying or have finished trying. Several said that they missed the support of the group once they were pregnant and that they also missed the clinic support. They were there on their own with all the anxieties of any new parents.

Those who have conceived may also be faced later with the possible choice of having further treatment to try for a second child. This was a very difficult area for several couples we spoke to. Some felt it was selfish or 'greedy' to try again when there were other couples still childless. Even when they had stored frozen embryos they were concerned about using finite clinic resources. Others were reluctant to go through the procedure again, dreading the clinic visits and further intrusion into their lives.

Ginny was a 35-year-old teacher who had conceived after three treatment cycles. She had not considered giving up at any time and says, 'I think I would have gone on and on. I was so fixed on having a baby. Once I was pregnant my antenatal care was transferred to my local hospital; my fertility treatment had been done 40 miles away. I didn't tell anyone at antenatal about the assisted conception, although I suppose they knew. I just wanted to be treated like everyone else. I felt a bit deceitful and underhand but I didn't want anyone to make my baby different. At 32 weeks I had some bleeding and they took me in for the last weeks for bed rest. It was actually a really good time; I was anxious at first but it all settled down and I felt reassured and safe. I don't think that until then I had wanted to admit how scared I was that the pregnancy would fail. The birth was fine and James was healthy. It was after I came home that I felt so alone. We had had support for years from the GP, the fertility clinic, the support group and then the hospital. Suddenly I was all alone and expected to cope. I fell apart after a month and was given medication. One of the worst aspects of it was that we had never told anyone about the fertility treatment so I felt that I had no-one to talk to. Paul went off to work and threw himself into that; I stayed at home trying to look after the baby I had wanted so much and now felt so confused by. I think it was the lack of support that was so hard. In the end it all came pouring out to a neighbour. She seemed understanding and caring and I couldn't hold it all in any longer. Then I was really worried that she would tell other people and that I would turn up at playgroup with James one day in the future and all the other mums would know.

Two years later I decided that we did not feel like a proper family with only one child and because of my age I thought we should try again soon. When I said this to Paul he was horrified. He wanted nothing more to do with assisted conception and said that he could not go *through it again. I suppose I hadn't realized the toll it had taken on him until then. I felt awful, let down, guilty and anxious. I didn't want to put Paul through something he hated but I wanted a proper family and one was never going to be that for me. Eventually we went to a Relate counsellor because our relationship deteriorated so badly. I feel that if we had talked through some of these things before it would not have happened. Once we had conceived it was all just treated as fine and no one considered there could be problems'.*

Ginny may have benefited by some time with a counsellor once her pregnancy was confirmed to allow her to consider all the implications of pregnancy. The move out of clinic support with the self-image of the infertile into the world where fertility was treated as everyday was a real problem to her. She had not really considered the difficulties of not having told anyone about the treatment so not everyone treated her the way she wanted and were not there when she needed them. The counsellor may have helped them as a couple to look at these areas. She also had no idea of where to go for help. The 'secret' had been so well entrenched that she found herself unable to ask her health visitor. A support group for mothers or the possibility of a connection to her previous support group may have helped.

Conception After Donor Insemination

Those who have conceived as a result of donor insemination (DI) may have different problems. They should have received counselling before the decision, and have talked through the implications of DI. However, they may find that once they are pregnant their feelings are affected in ways they did not anticipate. During pregnancy there may be tensions about being a 'proper' parent and how involved the other partner may be able to become. There are also all the normal tensions that arise from pregnancy with a fear and anxiety about the future.

Dean was 34 when he and his wife decided to use a donor. He had been told 2 years before that he had a very low sperm count. He had found this difficult and became guilty about 'being different'; he was unable to talk about it to Sarah, his partner, and they did not proceed with treatment at that time. 'Our relationship was not very good. I knew Sarah was hoping every month and I started to feel that I was failing her in everything. I gave up a good job really through lack of confidence. I recognized our relationship was getting into real trouble and we had to do something. When DI was eventually suggested I was horrified; it was like Sarah having another man because I was useless. We did discuss this with the counsellor and with our GP who were both prepared to give us a lot of time. I took about a year to come round to the idea. It didn't work the first time and very selfishly I felt a bit relieved – someone else had failed. All the time I really did want children or at least one, and when it succeeded next time I was excited and very pleased. We had talked about the possible problems of DI for us as a couple but I was upset by how bad I felt towards the end of the pregnancy. We decided not to tell anyone that it was donor, although the family and close friends knew we had been to the clinic. One of the things I dreaded was people saying it was like me; I worried a lot about what I would say. I also felt that it was really Sarah's baby and I was there to support her and thought I might find it hard to treat the baby the same as if it had been mine.'

Dean felt that it would have been helpful if he could have talked freely with someone about his doubts. He could not talk to Sarah, as he felt that he wanted to be as supportive as possible and not burden her with his feelings. He also felt that it was wrong to be upset with her that she was so happy about it and he felt sad and angry that it was not his child. After the birth of the baby, Dean was initially still worried that 'at some point I might look at my son and think he's not really mine at all, but in fact I've never once thought that. I am so much his father and I know he will never know any other father that biology doesn't seem to count for much'.

The lack of information about the donor may lead to fantasies about this person and what they are like; they have an intimate part in their lives, yet are strangers. During pregnancy and certainly after birth there is an importance placed on 'identifying' the baby, which may be difficult for the parents of DI children. Remarks such as 'he looks just like your uncle Tom', from unknowing family may be difficult to handle if they have not been anticipated. This is particularly so if the couple feel vulnerable or stigmatized by using assisted conception.

It may help the couple to be encouraged to examine together what the fantasies may be about the donor. This applies as much to a lesbian couple as to a heterosexual partnership. Although they will have received counselling before embarking on DI, the feelings they have once the baby is 'real' may be different and they may be allowing themselves to explore new avenues that were closed to them when they were focused on getting pregnant. There is still a great deal of uncertainty as to whether to tell the children of their genetic origins. The Royal College of Obstetricians and Gynaecologists (RCOG) in 1987 advised recipients that 'unless you reveal . . . to your child, there is no reason for him or her to know that he or she was conceived by donor insemination'.

It is important that the parents agree on whether to tell the child or not. They may find that it is a very big secret to carry even if there is no chance of the child ever finding out. There is a possibility of disagreement between the partners in this area and one they may need to explore with the counsellor. It is not something on which there can be compromise and it may be that the wishes of one partner will be over-ridden. As DI has not been established long enough for there to be a body of research on

165

telling the children, some have looked towards adoption as the model. Here most adoptees who are told of their birth parents from their earliest times are able to accept this. They do, however, often want to know about their birth parents and sometimes to meet them or at least make contact with them as adults. This is not going to be possible for the children born from donor gametes and there is often very little information available to them. Counselling services may be needed to help these young people. The King's Fund Committee (1991) suggested that counselling should cover:

- the applicant's motivation for seeking information
- the applicant's reaction to awareness of his/her donor conception
- the applicant's expectations in seeking information
- the possible consequences of this information for the applicant.

These are very much like the guidelines established for those adoptees seeking to find their birth parents and there is considerable expertise established in this area.

Counselling for Pregnancy

The people who discussed their feelings with us felt that counselling for a pregnancy by assisted conception was very important. They felt that it needed to concentrate on the partners' reactions to being parents. It is a time to look forward and to explore feelings about having a child and becoming a family. It is necessary for the parents to recognize that they will change and be changed by the experience of parenthood and that this can be a liberating as well as a frightening prospect. They also need to accept the need for flexibility. When people have been focused, often for many years, on being a parent, it is easy to develop ideas of how you will be and how you will feel. This may not happen and you need to feel open to change and able to change together.

Parents should also be encouraged by the research findings of Golombok *et al.* (1993) who found in a study of families created by assisted conception that 'the quality of parenting in families

166

with a child conceived by assisted conception is superior to that shown by families with a naturally conceived child. No group differences were found for any of the measures of children's emotions, behaviour or relationships with parents'.

Counselling for Ending Treatment Without a Pregnancy

The decision to end treatment, whether it is taken by the patients or by the treatment centre, is the end of the hopes and dreams of becoming parents by giving birth. This loss needs to be acknowledged and the clients helped to move on. The moving on can only begin with the recognition that there is no possibility of change. Even if they are holding onto a small chance that it will be all right next time, the couple will be unable to move forward. For those who have devoted a great deal of time, money and emotional energy to the pursuit of treatment it may be hard to come to terms with ending. They may seek to prolong treatment or start to explore other means. If there has been good counselling during the process of diagnosis and treatment then the possibility of childlessness may have been addressed and feelings about this explored and discussed. If this has not been possible the counsellor will need to help the clients to recognize the reality of their situation. They may be encouraged then to see ending not as a reaction to failure but as a positive choice. Empowering people to make positive choices and feel in control of their lives is a very important part of counselling. Ending treatment can be seen as a turning point in their lives.

For those attending a treatment centre with a counsellor it may be part of the counselling role to help the clients to decide to stop treatment or to help them accept the decision of the clinic. It is not the role of the counsellor to make the decision, even though some clients may try to pass that responsibility onto the counsellor, but the counsellor can be helpful in giving permission to the clients to make their choice, and not feel that they must pursue treatment at all costs. This may best be done by reflecting techniques, helping them to recognize their feelings about endings and loss. The counsellor may need to help the clients deal together and separately with the feelings of loss that may be engendered by the decision to end treatment. There is a considerable body of work on counselling for loss and some of the theoretical principles are relevant to the loss of infertility.

This first stage of recognition is echoed in the work of several therapists who write about the process of grieving after bereavement. Although this is not a bereavement, many infertile couples feel the need to find a focus for their feelings of loss. This is the loss of the longed for child, the loss of a potential role as parent and for some the loss of femininity or masculinity as part of the process. Murray Parkes (1972) writes of the process of realization, that is 'the way the bereaved moves from denial or avoidance of the recognition of loss towards acceptance'. For many infertile people they have accepted their infertility by this time but have not necessarily accepted their childlessness. To reach this stage of acceptance, Kubler-Ross (1970) believes that the individual must go through stages of denial and isolation, anger, bargaining and depression. Many clients of infertility clinics would say that they have experienced all of these feelings during the process of diagnosis and treatment. Kubler-Ross describes the acceptance stage as '. . . not a happy stage. It is almost void of feelings'. She acknowledges that some people find it almost impossible to reach acceptance. They go on struggling, sometimes believing that it is cowardly to give up. They may be helped by being given the possibility of choice, thus encouraging them to take control and lose some of the feelings of helplessness that are part of mourning a loss.

William Worden (1983) offers 10 principles of counselling for normal grief. These begin with helping the person to actualize the loss. In working with the infertile client this means helping them to talk about their experiences in order to make them real. They can then go on to express their feelings about the loss, their anger, guilt and sadness. Worden also recommends that grief counselling be offered as continuing support, allowing those who have experienced loss to deal with it at their own speed and to be able to continue to express their feelings. They can then move on to examine their own coping mechanisms, with the counsellor helping to identify them and to enable the client to see how effective they are and whether they need to try alternatives. Where this is not possible within the treatment clinic, the patients may be referred to loss counselling elsewhere.

Once the person has been able to recognize and accept the

time to end treatment, they can then start to move on with their lives and look at the positives. However, it also means facing the world with the reality. It may be that they will have to say to someone 'we are not going to have children' or 'we are not able to have children'. They may be faced with the effects on family and community of this fact and have to deal with their feelings as well. For those who feel that life has been 'on hold' for some time, they may be able to be helped, given permission, to let this go and take all the opportunities they can to live their lives as they would like to. There may be some residual feeling that this is selfish and the couples may need to express their feelings about this to each other. They may need time and information to consider their options about parenthood by other means or they may need to learn to enjoy just being together as a couple. The counsellor can also help by accepting that the couple may not reach these stages at the same time, and they can support each other even though they are at different stages of recognition and acceptance.

This may also be true of their feelings about other means of becoming a family, such as surrogacy or adoption. These steps will need to be taken in agreement with one another. Parenting for one may only be possible if it is biologically their child. There is no compromise. All of these possibilities require the clients to be given all the conditions that we have suggested were important at the very beginning: information, recognition and exploration of feelings, and an acceptance that at the end of what may feel like considerable intrusion, there are no guarantees.

Just as at all steps along the path of infertility recognition, diagnosis and treatment, the people who spoke to us and answered the questionnaires wanted support, acceptance and genuine concern from those who dealt with them. Some recognized a need for more in-depth counselling; all felt a need for information, advice, understanding, and time and space to talk.

REFERENCES

Burnard, P. (1989) *Counselling Skills for Health Professionals*, London: Chapman & Hall.

Egan, G. (1982) *The Skilled Helper*, 2nd edn, Balmont, CA: Wadsworth.

Golombok, S., Cook, R., Bish, A. and Murray, C., (1993) Quality of parenting in families created by the new reproductive technologies. *Journal of Psychosomatic Obstetrics and Gynaecology* **14**, 17–22.

King's Fund (1991) *Counselling for Regulated Infertility Treatments*, Report of the King's Fund Centre Counselling Committee, London.

Kubler-Ross, E. (1970) *On Death and Dying*, London: Tavistock.

Murray Parkes, C. (1972) *Bereavement Studies of Grief in Adult Life*, London: Tavistock.

Royal College of Obstetricians and Gynaecologists (1987) *Donor Insemination*, London: RCOG.

Worden, J.W. (1983) *Grief Counselling and Grief Therapy*, London: Tavistock.

Further Reading

Anton, L. (1992) *Never to be a Mother*, London: Harper Collins.

Badinter, E. (1982) *The Myth of Motherhood*, London: Souvenir Press.

Birke, L., Himmelweit, S. and Vinis, G. (1990) *Tomorrow's Child: Reproductive Technologies in the 90s*, London: Virago.

Blyth, E. (1995) *Infertility and Assisted Conception: Practice Issues for Counsellors*, Birmingham, UK: British Association of Social Workers (BASW).

British Medical Association (1996) *Changing Conceptions of Motherhood*, London: BMA.

Cotton, K. and Winn, D. (1985) *Baby Cotton – For Love and Money*, London: Dorling Kindersley.

Dryden, W. (1990) *Individual Therapy: A Handbook*, Milton Keynes: Open University Press.

Griel, A. (1991) *Not Yet Pregnant*, New Brunswick: Rutgers.

Houghton D. and Houghton P. (1987) *Coping With Childlessness*, London: Unwin.

Ironside, V. and Biggs, S. (1995) *The Subfertility Handbook*, London: Sheldon Press.

Jones, M. (1991) *Infertility: Modern Treatments and the Issues They Raise*, London, Piatkus.

Kennedy, E. and Charles, S. (1977) *On Becoming A Counsellor. A Basic Guide for Non-Professionals*, Dublin: Gill & Macmillan.

Lasker, J. and Borg, S. (1987) *In Search of Parenthood*, London: Pandora.

Mason, M-C. (1993) *Male Infertility: Men Talking*, London: Routledge.

Pepperall, R., Hudson, R. and Woods, C. (Eds) (1980) *The Infertile Couple*, Edinburgh: Churchill Livingstone.

171

Pfeffer, N. and Woollett, A. (1983) *The Experience of Infertility,* London: Virago.

Read, J. (1995) *Counselling for Fertility Problems,* London: Sage.

Rehner, J. (1989) *Infertility: Old Myths, New Meanings,* Toronto, Canada: Second Story Press.

Salzer, L. (1986), *Surviving Infertility,* London: Harper Collins.

Snowden, R. and Mitchell, G.D. (1981) *The Artificial Family,* London: Allen & Unwin.

Snowden, R. and Snowden, E. (1993) *The Gift of a Child: A Guide to Donor Insemination,* Exeter: University of Exeter Press.

Templeman, A. and Drife, J. (1992) *Infertility,* Berlin, Heidelberg and New York: Springer-Verlag.

Veevers, J. (1980) *Childless by Choice,* Toronto: Butterworth.

Winston, R. (1987) *Infertility: A Sympathetic Approach,* London: Macdonald Optima.

Glossary

Amenorrhoea – complete cessation of menstrual periods. Primary when the woman has never bled and secondary when the woman has had no bleeding for 6 months or more.

Anovulation – failure to ovulate.

Azoospermia – abscence of any sperm in the ejaculate.

Bromocriptine – drug used to suppress high levels of prolactin.

Buserelin/Nafarelin – GnRH analogues that initially stimulate the pituitary but when continued suppress the pituitary and its production of gonadotrophins.

Chlamydia – organism that causes widespread infection in the genital tract. Is a known cause of tubal damage.

Chromosomes – small structures within each cell containing the genetic material that controls all functions and characteristics of that cell. Each cell should contain 46 chromosomes.

Clomiphene citrate (Clomid) – mild fertility drug often used to stimulate ovulation as a first-line treatment.

Cryopreservation – freezing of spare embryos in liquid nitrogen.

Cystic fibrosis – genetically inherited disease in which secretions are abnormally thick and viscid.

Danazol – drug used in the medical treatment of endometriosis.

Donor insemination (DI) – artificial insemination with donor sperm.

Endometriosis – cells forming the lining of the womb proliferate.

Epididymis – convoluted tube that lies above the testicle and conveys semen to the vas deferens.

Follicles – the sacs on the ovary in which oocytes develop.

Follicle stimulating hormone (FSH) – a hormone produced by the pituitary gland which stimulates follicles to develop in the ovary.

173

Gamete intra fallopian transfer (GIFT) – treatment for infertility in which oocytes are retreived at laparoscopy and returned to the fallopian tubes with sperm.

Genetic abnormality/disorder – abnormality in the hereditary factors present in the chromosomes in the germ cell.

Gonadotrophins – collective name for FSH and LH.

Gonadotrophin releasing hormone (GnRH) – produced in the hypothalamus; this hormone stimulates the pituitary.

GnRH anologue – see buserelin/nafarelin.

Human chorionic gonadotrophin (hCG) – hormone produced by the pituitary gland that is similar in action to leutinizing hormone (LH). It is given to trigger ovulation in stimulated cycles.

Human menopausal gonadotrophins (hMG) – drug containing pure FSH or FSH and LH and used in induction of ovulation. Recombinant hMG is now being manufactured genetically.

Hypothalmic–pituitary–ovarian axis – relationship between the hypothalmus and the pituitary, both hormone-producing glands, and the ovary, on which the hormones are working.

In vitro **fertilization (IVF/IVF-ET)** – fertilizing sperm with oocytes and the laboratory transfer of resulting embryos.

Intracytoplasmic sperm injection (ICSI) – injection of a single sperm into the nucleus of the oocyte to enhance fertilization.

Intrauterine insemination (IUI) – injecting sperm through the cervix directly into the uterus.

Laparoscopy – surgical assessment of the overall anatomy of the pelvis with particular reference to tubal patency.

Luteinizing hormone (LH) – a hormone produced by the pituitary gland that suddenly surges and causes final maturation of the oocyte within the follicle. Ovulation occurs about 36 hours after the LH surge.

Luteinizing hormone releasing hormone (LHRH) – the same as GnRH.

Menopause – cessation of menstrual periods and ovarian failure. Premature menopause may occur at any age.

Micro-epididymal sperm aspiration (MESA) – surgical removal of sperm from the epididymis.

Morphology – the structure and shape of a cell, in this case sperm. Quoted in sperm analysis as a percentage that have normal shape and structure.

Oligospermia – low sperm count in the ejaculate, i.e. below the accepted norm of 20 million per millilitre.

Ovarian hyperstimulation syndrome (OHSS) – complication of medical induction of ovulation.The ovaries become enlarged and filled with fluid. Symptoms range from mild to severe.

Parenteral induction of ovulation (PIO) – ovulation induced with the use of drugs, hMG and hCG.

Partial zonal dissection (PZD) – technique employed in IVF to break open the outer shell of the oocyte to enhance the passage of the sperm into the oocyte.

Pelvic inflammatory disease (PID) – refers to infection within the female genital tract usually the fallopian tubes. It is the most common cause of tubal blocking the causative organisms may be sexually transmitted.

Pentoxifylline – drug used to increase sperm motility.

Percutaneous epididymal sperm aspiration (PESA) – insertion of a fine needle into the epididymis under local anaesthetic to retrieve sperm.

Pituitary gland – located at the base of the brain, this gland produces a large number of hormones including FSH, LH and prolactin.

Polycystic ovaries – particular appearance of the ovaries as seen on ultrasound scan or at laparoscopy. The ovaries are larger than normal with a smooth thick outer layer and contain multiple cysts.

Polycystic ovarian disease/syndrome (PCOD/S) – syndrome that features polycystic ovaries, menstrual disturbances, obesity, hirsutism, raised LH and symptoms of increased testosterone production. Not necessarily all present in every case.

Progesterone – hormone produced by the corpus luteum after ovulation. It causes the secretory changes in the endometrium in preparation for the embryo to embed.

Prolactin – hormone produced in the pituitary which if present in large amounts causes milk secretion and cessation of menstrual periods.

Retrograde ejaculation – sperm are ejaculated backwards into the bladder instead of forwards along the urethra.

Subzonal insemination (SUZI) – insertion of sperm under the zona pellucida (the outer shell) of the oocyte.

Tamoxifen – drug that has the same use and effect as clomiphene citrate.

175

Testes/testicles – two glands in the scrotum that produce sperm.

Testicular epididymal sperm aspiration (TESA) – removal of the sperm from the testes.

Testosterone – male hormone produced by specialist cells in the testes.

Thyroid stimulating hormone (TSH) – this hormone stimulates the thyroid gland to produce thyroxine. Over or under activity of the thyroid may affect ovulation.

Tubal occlusion – damage to the inside of the fallopian tubes severe enough to cause complete blockage.

Vas deferens – the tube from each testicle that carries the sperm into the urethra.

Zygote intrafallopian transfer (ZIFT) – transfer at the pronuclear stage of development, which occurs the day after fertilization.

Appendix

Useful Organizations and Addresses

British Agencies for Adoption and
  Fostering
Skyline House
200, Union St
London SE1 0LY

British Association for
  Counselling (register of courses
  and accredited counsellors)
1, Regent Place
Rugby
Warwicks CV21 2PJ

British Infertility Counselling
  Association
10, Alwyne Place
London N1 2NL

British Pregnancy Advisory
  Service
Austy Manor
Wooten Waven
Solihull
W. Midlands B95 6BX

CHILD (support for those with
  infertility problems)
Charter House
43, St. Leonards Road
Bexhill-on-Sea
East Sussex TN40 1JA

Childlessness Overcome Through
  Surrogacy (COTS)
Loandhu Cottage
Gruids
Lairg
Sutherland IV27 4EF

DI Network (donor insemination
  support group)
PO Box 265
Sheffield S3 7VX

Family Planning Association
27, Mortimore St
London W1N 7RJ

Gay & Lesbian Foster Carers
  Association
c/o London Friend
86, Caledonian Rd
London N1 9DN

Huamn Fertilization and
  Embryology Authority
Paxton House
30, Artillery Lane
London E1 7LS

Infertility Support Group
Women's Health and
    Reproductive Rights
52–4, Featherstone St
London EC1Y 8RT

ISSUE (The National Fertility
    Association)
509, Aldridge Rd
Great Barr
Birmingham B44 8NA

Miscarriage Association (national
    information and local groups)
c/o Clayton Hospital
Northgate
Wakefield
West Yorkshire WF1 3JS

Multiple Births Foundation
Institute of Obstetrics and
    Gynaecology
Queen Charlotte's Hospital
Goldhawk Rd
London W6 0XG

National Foster Care Association
Francis House
Francis St
London SW1 1DE

National Organization for
    Counselling Adoptees and
    Parents (NORCAP)
3, New High St
Headington
Oxford OX3 7AJ

Parent to Parent Information on
    Adoption Services
Lower Boddington
Daventry
Northants NN11 6YB

Pregnancy Advisory Service
11–13, Charlotte St
London W1P 1HD

Stillbirth and Neonatal Death
    Society
28, Portland Place
London W1N 4DE

STORK (national group for
    parents adopting from
    overseas)
Dan Y Graig Cottage
Balaclava Rd
Glais
Swansea SA7 9HJ

Support for Termination for
    Abnormality
National Office
22, Upper Woburn Place
London WC1H 0EP

Training Organizations

The Actors Institute
137, Goswell Rd
London EC1 (Dance and Drama
    Therapy)

Association for Group and
    Individual Psychotherapy
1, Fairbridge Rd
London N19 3EN

Association for Humanistic
   Psychology
26, Huddlestone Rd
London E7 0AN

British Association of Art
   Therapists
11a Richmond Rd
Brighton
Sussex BN2 3RL

British Association for
   Counselling,
1, Regent Place
Rugby
Warwicks CV21 2PJ

British Association for
   Psychotherapy
121, Hendon Lane
London NW3 7RD

Norwich Centre for Personal and
   Professional Development
7, Earlham Rd
Norwich NR2 3RA

Gestalt Centre
64, Warwick Rd
St Albans
Herts AL1 4DL

Institute of Psychosynthesis
The Barn
Nan Clarks Lane
Mill Hill
London NW7 4HH

Institute of Transactional Analysis
BM Box 4104
London WC1N 3XX

National College of Hypnosis and
   Psychotherapy
12, Cross St
Nelson
Lancashire BB0 7EN

Westminster Pastoral Foundation
23, Kensington Square
London W8 5HN

179

Index